Soil
Signals

A practical guide
to a fertile soil

ROODBONT
| AGRICULTURAL PUBLISHERS

LOUIS BOLK
INSTITUUT

Credits

Authors

Chris Koopmans
Jan Bokhorst
Coen ter Berg
Nick van Eekeren
The authors are associated with the Louis Bolk Institute.

Editors

Chris Koopmans and Ton van Schie

Translation

Luppo Diepenbroek, Straight Line Nutrition Ltd

Content editor

David Hogan BSc CSci, Environmental Consultant

Proofreading

Agrolingua

Special thanks to

Jaap Brink, Marjolein Hanegraaf, Wied Hendrix, Harm Keidel, Stephan Mantel, Gerard Oomen, Durk Oosterhof, Bert Philipsen, Udo Prins, Arjan Reijneveld, Eugène Thijssen, Frans Tijink, Aaldrik Venhuizen, Erna van der Wal, Marleen Zanen

Photography

Jan Bokhorst, Coen ter Berg, Nick van Eekeren and Chris Koopmans. Anna de Weerd and Marleen Zanen.
Also: Alterra (7, 9, 10, 11), Altic (39), ASG (84, 85), BLGG AgroXpertus (39), Bureau voor Beeld Wageningen (36, 72), CLM (90), FAO-UNESCO (6), ISRIC World Soil Information (8, 9, 10, 11, 13), K+S Benelux (16, 17, 18,19), Kverneland (52, 53, 54, 59, 60, 61), Kruse Ootmarsum (55), Yakov Kuzyakov (7, 9, 11, 13), LaMi (53), Marco van Liere (82, 88), Durk Oosterhof (67, 73, 83), Gerda Peters (31), PPO (33, 92, 93), PRI (32), Udo Prins (88, 89), U. Schuler (9, 12), Frans Tijink (57), Universiteit van Gent (87), University of Delaware (8), University of Tennessee (32), J. Verschoore (20), www.freedigitalphotos.net (7).

Cover image based on photo by Michiel Wijnbergh.

Illustrations

Gerda Peters, Fingerprint

Design

bhgo, ontwerp voor web en druk
Studio Hiddink

Roodbont Publishers B.V.
P.O. Box 4103
7200 BC Zutphen
The Netherlands
T +31 (0)575 54 56 88
E info@roodbont.com
I www.roodbont.com

Louis Bolk Instituut (LBI)
Hoofdstraat 24
3972 LA Driebergen
The Netherlands
T +31 (0)343 52 38 60
E info@louisbolk.nl
I www.louisbolk.org

This edition was produced with financial and facilitating assistance from the Ministries of Infrastructure and the Environment and Economic Affairs.

ISBN 978-90-8740-157-3

Table of contents

Examining the soil

Economically profitable agriculture starts with fertile soil. This involves effective management. Soil is often ignored when looking at costs, prices and regulations, but we can learn and profit from managing it.

Environmental regulations can make farmers fearful about using too much fertiliser, but the result can be that soil fertility becomes too low. Leaching of nitrate and phosphate through soil into ground and surface water needs to be avoided as much as possible. By matching soil quality and nutrient management, we should be able to use less fertiliser without any loss of production. Farm management including maintaining soil fertility is the basis for profitable production. This also gives a socially acceptable return on investment.

Soil Signals is produced for farmers in the arable, livestock and horticulture sectors. When they venture 'underground', farmers find that soil is so much more than just a chemical analysis, and that it is not boring, but interesting!

Learning soil signals by looking, asking and understanding how they work will contribute to better farm management. Advisors and teachers can also learn from this Soil Signals book.

Soil
Signals

Soil Signals is not a text book, but a handbook. It uses pictures and drawings to show the types of signals presented by the soil. The examples and tables will get you climbing off the tractor and digging around in the soil yourself. What can you see? And what do you do next? The information connects your observations with what you want to achieve.

This handbook takes you from the big picture right down to the detail. First we look at the soils and the landscape above ground. Next up are soil types and structures. Soil has chemical, physical and biological characteristics which you can think of as a triangle, with each corner interacting to drive soil processes.

Information comes from soil analysis as well as observing and touching organic matter and soil biota (living soil organisms).

How you use this information will become clearer as you read this book: the chapters on soil preparation, fertilisation and crop rotation form a clear link between observation and farm activity. Let's get started!

Can you dig it?

In this book you will often come across a section entitled 'Back to Basics'. You can use this to see how well you understand the soil. Once you understand the soil, many other farming practices will become clearer.

The evolution of the farmer
Throughout history, the farmer has literally and figuratively become further removed from the soil. It's time to get your hands dirty again!

Chapter 1

Soils of the world

There are hundreds of types of soil in the world – too many to list them all here.

However, we can briefly mention some main groups that occur all over the world.

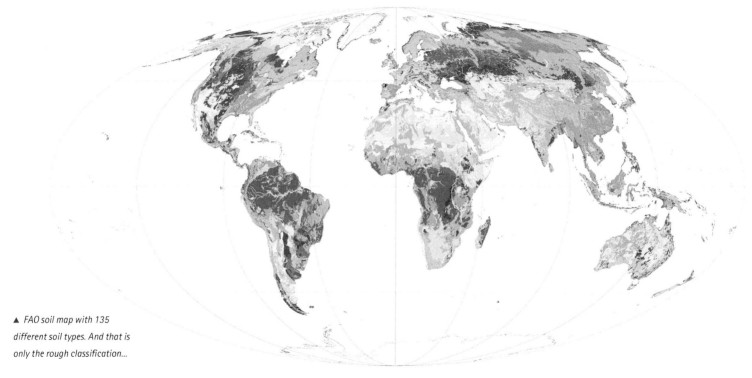

▲ *FAO soil map with 135 different soil types. And that is only the rough classification...*

The parent material in which soils develop, the climate, the landscape and the vegetation all have an impact on the development of soil. And on the other hand, soils support only a limited range of vegetation types, even when it comes to agricultural crops. That is why agricultural use depends so heavily on the type of soil. Human interventions such as cultivation and fertilisation do have an impact but they will not change a soil's basic characteristics. Actions such as drainage, however, will.

Soil Signals

Podzols

Podzols occur in areas of high rainfall, predominantly with coniferous trees or under heathy vegetation. This soil type is characterised by acidic leaf litter on the surface and a dark, organic-rich topsoil. Immediately underneath is an ash-grey layer, followed by black and orange-brown layers which gradually transitions into the original subsoil.

Many minerals, in particular iron- and aluminium-bearing compounds, have been leached out of the ash-grey layer. The black and brown layers have these colours due to the accumulation of humic substances from the litter layer. The soil is predominantly sand. In the tropics, podzols are usually sandy or gravelly, formed in quartzitic sands with tree species with extensive, shallow root systems.

Pine forest. ▼

Properties

Podzols are acidic soils. Because podzols are often formed in impoverished sands, they provide few nutrients for crops. The leaching of minerals impoverishes them even further. The dark accumulated layer is often highly compressed and not accessible for plant roots. Aluminium toxicity can occur.

Agricultural use

Podzolic soils have limited potential for agricultural use. But they do have some potential for forestry and extensive grazing, often on heathy vegetation important for nature conservation.

Their agricultural potential can be improved with drainage or subsoiling, soil working up to a depth of approximately 40 cm, liming and application of fertilisers. Relatively high levels of fertilisers are needed.

Podzol distribution around the world

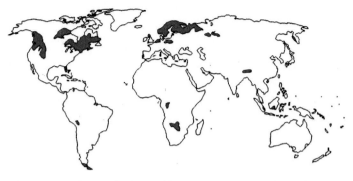

▲ *There are 485 million ha of podzolic soil in boreal and temperate regions and approx. 10 million in the tropics.*

Podzol developed in cover sand in northern Germany. ▼   *Podzol in sandy soil.* ▼

 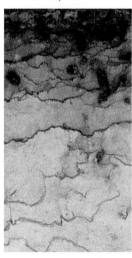

Cambisols

Cambisols are young soils only moderately developed by weathering, and brownish or reddish in colour. Organic matter is homogeneously distributed over a relatively thick layer. In Europe they are located mainly to the south of the podzol areas. In the northern hemisphere they frequently occur in alluvial and aeolian deposits. In the tropics and subtropics they occur on slopes but also in fluvial deposits and eroding lands. The largest uninterrupted area of cambisols is located in the deposits of the Ganges-Brahmaputra system. They have arisen under different types of vegetation, but mixed deciduous forests are very common.

Summit of Wuyi Mountains in China on Endoleptic Cambisol (Alumic Humic Skeletic). ▼

Properties

Because there are usually no intervening layers to impede drainage or root development, and there is a slightly thicker organic-matter-containing layer, they are reasonable or good for agricultural use. Most cambisols have good structural stability, high porosity, a good water-holding capacity and good internal drainage.

Agricultural use

Agricultural use depends very much on the climate. Cambisols in the temperate zone can be very productive.
In steep lands they are mainly used for grazing and forestry. In arid regions they are widely used, after irrigation, for arable and oil crops. In tropical regions cambisols are slightly richer than the more common acrisols and ferralsols.

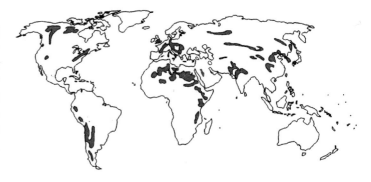

▲ *Altogether there are approx. 1,200 million ha of cambisols, about 500 million of which are suitable for use as arable land.*

Cambisol in Maryland (USA). ▼

Cambisol in Germany. ▼

Soil Signals

Chernozems

The original vegetation in areas with chernozems is predominantly grass of steppe regions. The roots are deep, and after a long time a thick, dark topsoil is created to a depth of up to 1.5m. Chernozems are fertile soils that are predominantly formed in loess. The climate is characterised by cold winters and warm, dry summers. Groundwater levels are deep. To the south of the chernozems the climate is dryer, and the organic-matter-rich layer is thinner and not black but brown in colour. These soils are called kastanozems.

Properties

The soils are suitable for deep root development and contain humus, and can in principle retain a lot of moisture. The organic matter content is generally above 5%. The soils have a neutral pH but become rich in calcium carbonate in the lower subsoil. Soil biota have ensured strong homogenisation of the profile. Because the summers in chernozem regions are often dry, drought is a serious problem. The organic matter content of kastanozems is lower than that of chernozems – usually 2-4%.

Agricultural potential

The high natural fertility of chernozems and their favourable topography permit a wide range of agricultural uses, including arable cropping, with supplementary irrigation in dry summers, and cattle ranging. Cereal growing, primarily wheat and barley, predominate. In the warmer southern areas, maize is also widely grown.

Distribution of chernozems and kastanozems

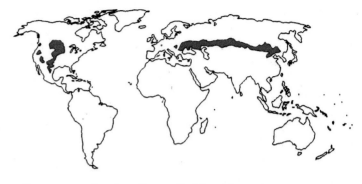

▲ *Chernozems occur in regions with very cold winters and warm, dry summers.*

Chernozem landscape in Polobino, Russian Federation. ▼

Chernozem near Heréd in Hungary. ▼

Kastanozem in Russia. ▼

Arenosols

Arenosols are sandy soils. The soils may have developed in recently deposited sands, older weathered sands or old quartz-rich material. Deserts and beach sands are also arenosols.

Properties

In arid and semi-arid environments, the sand is often bleached. The organic matter content is generally less than 1%.

The bleached topsoil has poor properties for agricultural use. After precipitation, the subsoil can remain dry. As a result, emergence of plant seeds does not readily take place. A platy structure and crust formation also prevent good germination. In consequence, in dry areas much of the land remains unvegetated. These soils are highly susceptible to soil erosion.

Agricultural use

In dry areas, extensive livestock farming is the main form of agriculture. The options for use increase with irrigation. Mixed arable cropping and raising is possible in temperate regions, particularly if supplementary irrigation is available in dry periods. Arenosols in the humid tropics are chemically exhausted and highly sensitive to erosion

Distribution of arenosols across the world

▲ *Arenosols occur in arid to humid and very cold to very hot regions.*

Landscape in Mali on a Ferralic Protic Rubic Arenosol (Eutric Aridic). ▼

Profile of an arenosol. ▼

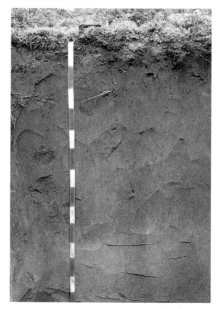

Fluvisols

Fluvisol refers to the Latin word fluvius (river), but fluvisol sediments can be fluvial, lacustrine or marine. Fluvisols occur all over the world in periodically flooded areas of alluvial plains, river fans, valleys and tidal marshes. They are young soils with limited indications of soil profile development; most variation results from layering within the alluvial material. Fluvisols formed in river alluvium can vary considerably in texture depending on their location in the floodplain. In the middle and lower stretches of the river, coarsely textured fluvisols are found on levees and more finely textured fluvisols in basins and backlands. They are regularly flooded with depositions of fresh material (unless the land has been empoldered) and show stratification and/or an irregular organic matter profile. In areas with marine sediments, coarse-textured fluvisols occur on barriers, cheniers, sand flats and crevasse splays, and finely textured fluvisols are found on clayey tidal flats and in chenier plains.

Properties

Soils can be wet in parts of the profile due to a fluctuating level of stagnating groundwater or flood water from rivers or tides. Terraces and river levees are much better drained than soils in low landscape positions.

Most fluvisols show mottling indicative of alternating reducing and oxidising conditions.

Agricultural use

Fluvisols are planted to annual crops and orchards and many are used for grazing. Flood control and drainage is normally required. Some fluvisols suffer from severe soil acidity and high levels of noxious Al-ions.

Landscape in the Netherlands on Humi-Gleyic Fluvisol (Eutric). ▼

Distribution of fluvisols across the world

▲ Areas with fluvisols represent important agricultural regions. Fifty percent of the world's population lives along rivers and coasts.

Fluvisol in northern Germany. ▼

Acrisols

The most important types of soil in the perhumid tropics and subtropics are acrisol. This occurs in areas with a sloping or hilly relief. In slightly flatter areas, acrisols commonly occur alongside ferrasols. Acrisols are formed of acid rock and are highly weathered in humid conditions under forest. Some acrisols are to be found in arid areas and date back to a more humid period in the distant past.

Properties

The most important clay mineral in acrisols is kaolinite. This has a much lower moisture- and nutrient-holding capacity than other clay minerals.
The soil profile has a homogenous structure with no clear stratification. Aluminium toxicity is very common on these soils. Phosphate retention is also a problem.

Agricultural use

These soils are acidic by nature. They are also very poor because nutrients are not retained efficiently. But the soil structure is good. They can be made into good agricultural soils with the addition of lime and fertilisers, though they can be very susceptible to erosion. On very acidic acrisols, only acid-loving crops like cashew nuts and bananas can be grown. Tea, rubber trees and oil palms can be grown on soils with aluminium toxicity. Coffee and sugar cane are also important crops. Shifting cultivation is also often applied.

Acrisol in Portugal. ▼

▲ *The total surface area of acrisols (red) is 1 billion ha. Of these, 500 million are suitable for agricultural use. Ferralsols also occur in the humid tropics (total 750 million ha, of which 300 million are suitable for growing crops). These are formed from basic rock, are less acidic and have more potential uses. Aluminium toxicity does not occur on these soils. In lixisoils – totalling 435 million ha, of which 150 million are suitable for growing crops – clay has been flushed from the topsoil to deeper layers. These soils are highly susceptible to soil erosion.*

Landscape and profile of a red acrisol in north-eastern Thailand. Yellow versions also occur. (Photos U. Schuler). ▼

Histosol

Histosols are soils formed in organic material, mainly peat. These vary from those soils developed predominantly in moss peat in boreal, arctic and subarctic regions, via moss peat, reeds/sedge peat and forest peat in temperate regions, to mangrove peat and swamp forest peat in the humid tropics. Histosols are found at all altitudes but the vast majority occur in lowlands. Organic soil material accumulates in conditions where decomposition of plant debris is slowed by:

- low temperatures,
- persistent water saturation of the soil body,
- extreme acidity or paucity of nutrient elements ('oligotrophy'), and/or
- high levels of electrolytes or organic toxins.

Histosols consist of incompletely decomposed plant remains, with or without admixtures of sand, silt or clay.

Properties

Transformation of plant remains through biochemical disintegration and formation of humic substances creates a surface layer of mould. Translocated organic material may accumulate in deeper layers, but is more often leached from the soil.

Agricultural use

Histosols are generally very difficult to cultivate because of their poor drainage and often low chemical fertility. However, histosols formed on very recent glacial lands can often be very productive when drained and produce high-grade pasture for dairying or beef cattle. When cultivated, there is a great risk of the organic matter becoming dry powder and eroding under the influence of wind. A tendency towards shrinkage and compaction is also evident with cropping. Natural peat bogs must be drained and normally also limed and fertilised, to permit cultivation of agricultural crops. In many instances, centrally guided reclamation projects opened up millions of hectares to agriculture, but this initiated the gradual degradation, and ultimately the loss, of the precious peat. In the tropics, increasing numbers of landless farmers venture out into the peat lands where they clear the forest and cause raging peat fires in the process. For the past few decades increasing areas of tropical peat land have been planted to oil palm and pulp wood tree species. This practice may be less than ideal but it is far less destructive than arable subsistence farming.

Distribution of histosol across the world

▲ Histosols occur extensively in boreal, arctic and subarctic regions. Elsewhere, they are confined to poorly drained basins, depressions, swamps and marshlands with shallow groundwater, and highland areas with a high precipitation/evapotranspiration ratio.

Histosol in northern Europe. ▼

Peat landscape in West-Kalimantan, Indonesia, where the peat is locally burned and planted with rice. ▼

Chapter 2

Nutrients and structure

The appearance of the sward or arable crop tells you about the structure, aeration and other factors affecting plant growth. Soil structure and chemistry provide the underlying conditions for plant growth.

Using structure signals. Waterlogging can tell you something about the soil structure. If after a heavy rain shower, water stays on the soil surface for more than a few hours, then there is likely to be something wrong with the soil structure at or just below the surface. ▼

▲ *A well established cereal crop has a dense root mass, which promotes good soil and is beneficial for nutrient cycling and structure in the future.*

Before we discuss the chemistry of the soil, let us take a look at some basic information on the physical characteristics of different soil types. The soil type itself can provide key information on the soil chemistry, as a medium and as a provider of nutrients. The different size particles that make up the soil have a characteristic feel. The proportion of different particle sizes is referred to as the soil texture. When you touch different soil textures with your hand, they will feel very different. This is the result of the particles that make up the soil: sand, silt and clay. Texture is crucial to the properties of the soil and cannot change suddenly. When you examine soils in the field you should also be sure to assess the texture of the different soil layers. These determine the properties of that soil. A soil texture with approximately the same amount of sand, silt and clay particles is called a loam.

Soil Signals

Sand

Sand grains are often visible to the naked eye (grain size is 50-2000 μm). Large pores develop between the large grains which are ideal for drainage but do not hold water well. Sand retains relatively low levels of moisture, due to the surface area being small in relation to the volume. Sand provides soil with stability, but does not help to retain any plant nutrients.

Silt

Silt particles are invisible to the naked eye. They are small (2-50 μm) and hence smaller pores occur between the grains. As a result of the small pores water is retained, but as with sand, nutrient retention is low. Silt does not stick to the fingers, and so very silty soils slip through the fingers like soap. Silty soils can be at risk of compaction, especially at the soil surface (slumping) and of erosion by water.

Clay

The clay particles are less than 2 μm. Clay soils can retain a large amount of water and also nutrients, but not all the water is available to be absorbed by the plant. A loamy soil contains up to 40 percent clay, above which it becomes a clay soil. As water and air pass slowly through clays, shortage of oxygen can occur easily. Because clay soils have large moisture-holding capacity, crops are more able to tolerate drying conditions and drought problems do not develop as quickly. Very dry clay can become like lumps of concrete.

Some types of clay can shrink and swell with changes in their moisture content.

Practical evaluation of soil types

	Sand	Loam	Silt	Clay
Particles visible	Yes	Few	No	No
Stability, dry clods	No clod formation	Easy to break	Very stable	Large, hard and compact
Stability, wet clods	Unstable	Moderately stable	Stable	Very stable
Ability to roll a thread between thumb and fingers (plasticity)	Does not form	Does not form	Thin and breakable	Very long and flexible

After Brady and Weil, 1996

You can feel the differences between the soils very easily. Rub a small clod of wet soil between your thumb and index finger. Sand feels grainy and falls apart, clay is smooth and shiny, and loams hold together well.

Chemistry in the soil: major elements

Understanding the supply from the soil is important for optimal utilisation of nutrients from inputs like fertilisers. Alongside this, it is important to minimise losses of nutrients, especially nitrogen and phosphorus. The use of nutrients is increasingly restricted by regulation aimed at minimising environmental pollution.

Nitrogen deficiency. This may be caused by a mistake in application or the restricted availability of nitrogen from the soil. Losses due to leaching or volatilisation can also restrict nitrogen availability for crops. Luckily there are many ways to rectify shortages. ▼

Nitrogen

Nitrogen is an important nutrient for the plant: it is a main component of proteins and is therefore essential for growth. Continued topping up is essential on agricultural soils. Nitrogen from most fertilisers is quickly available to plants. The nitrogen from other sources is mostly associated with carbon, and first has to be released. Nitrogen becomes available to the plant following breakdown of organic matter in the soil (mineralisation); nitrogen from crop residues, legumes and organic manures is also released for plants through mineralisation. How quickly this happens depends on the temperature and the moisture content of the soil. Nitrogen deficiency expresses itself in a lower crop yield and often in the lighter colour of the leaf during growth. An excess of nitrogen makes the plant more susceptible to diseases, especially fungal diseases, and weakens the stem, leading to premature lodging of cereals.

Phosphorus deficiency in maize. Growth remains retarded and the plant colour darkens. With severe deficiency leaves become red or purple. This can point towards low phosphorus supply or low availability as a result of poor soil structure or low temperatures. In this case it is due to cold conditions; when the weather becomes warmer the colour disappears. ▶

Phosphorus

Phosphorus is essential for good growth. It is a component of cell membranes and essential to support energy transfers in the plant. Phosphorus becomes available to the plant by breakdown of organic matter, in organic manures and in plant available forms in fertilisers. As with nitrogen, temperature and moisture play a part in making phosphorus available. Soil phosphates are poorly soluble in water, as they are strongly tied to iron and calcium and are therefore relatively immobile. Roots can create mildly acidic conditions around them, through which phosphorus bonds are broken and phosphorus released for plant uptake. Unlike nitrogen, phosphorus barely moves in soil, so the roots have to grow towards the released phosphorus. Good soil structure for effective rooting is therefore more important for phosphorus uptake than for nitrogen.

Potassium

Potassium plays an important part in a crop's water balance, resistance to diseases and in enhancing plant properties, such as taste and durability. Potassium is available in solution in the soil and can leach from soil, especially from sandy soils. Potassium can also be found attracted to clay and humus surfaces. Young clay soils contain minerals which release potassium. Decreases in fertiliser applications over the last few years mean that potassium deficiencies are more common, especially in silage or maize crops.

Deficiency symptoms of some nutrients

Deficiency	Symptom
Nitrogen	Even, light colour in old leaves, occasionally with red tint in cold weather
Phosphorus	Dark leaves, also red or purple
Potassium	Brown edges
Magnesium	Light colour between nerves, particularly on older leaves
Sulphur	Even, light colour in young leaves
Manganese	Light colour between nerves, particularly in younger leaves
Boron	Base of youngest leaves discoloured
Zinc	Small leaves, partly dying off
Molybdenum	Brown edges
Copper	Light colour
Calcium	Tip of youngest leaves dying off
Silicon	Weak crop susceptible to diseases

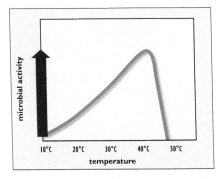

◄ Temperature has a strong influence on making nitrogen available. Nitrogen deficiency in the spring is often caused by a soil temperature that is too low. The topsoil temperature runs approximately five days behind the average daily temperature.

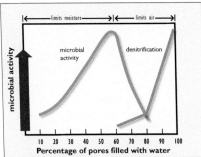

◄ Drought results in slower growth. However, the plant is not just deficient in moisture, but also nitrogen. Nitrogen is not released in a dry soil, and therefore the flow to the plant is limited. Once it starts to rain nitrogen will become available in most cases by itself. Under wet conditions due to a lack of oxygen, nitrogen becoming available in the soil is reduced. In addition, it is lost through bacterial transformations as a gas (denitrification).

◄ Potassium deficiency in wheat. In many crops potassium deficiency shows as brown points on the leaves. However, before this occurs, a potassium deficiency can already exist.

Sulphur

The reduction in air pollution in recent years has resulted in a decline in sulphur deposition to agricultural soils, so sulphur deficiency on agricultural soils is a new phenomenon. Sulphur is an essential element in protein synthesis and hence growth. Sulphur deficiency expresses itself as an even, light colour in plants, similar to nitrogen deficiency. With sulphur the young leaf is slightly lighter, while with nitrogen the older leaf is discoloured. Sulphur deficiency is seen mainly in sulphur-sensitive crops such as brassicas. Crops like winter wheat and grass, which have already started growth by early spring, can also show sulphur deficiency. This occurs because of insufficient mineralisation in early spring. Most other crops are able to meet their sulphur requirements from mineralisation. Sulphur comes from the breakdown of organic matter, from organic and mineral fertilisers and from the air. Plant uptake of sulphur is predominantly in the form of sulphate. The highest risk of deficiency is on light, easily leachable soils.

Magnesium

Magnesium is a key component of chlorophyll, and the plant becomes pale in colour when a deficiency arises. Magnesium is attracted to humus and clay surfaces in the soil, but is leached following heavy rainfall, particularly from sandy soils. Both organic and mineral fertilisers are good sources of magnesium. It is important that magnesium is in a good balance with other nutrients, especially potassium and calcium, which are also attracted to the surfaces of soil material.

Trace elements

Trace elements are needed in small quantities, but they are no less important because of this. Deficiencies are rare when organic manures are used and where soil pH is managed carefully. Deficiency symptoms often manifest themselves when mineral fertiliser is the main fertiliser used. However, imbalances in other nutrients can lead to trace element deficiency: e.g. excess phosphorus can cause problems with uptake of copper, zinc and manganese. Trace element deficiency symptoms are usually difficult to recognise. Combining plant and soil analysis can help identify a deficiency and its cause. Always ensure a good supply of trace elements via fertilisers and maintain a good pH.

Sulphur deficiency in oilseed rape. Sulphur deficiency symptoms are mainly seen in brassicas, winter wheat and grass. One symptom is the light colour. The difference between this and nitrogen deficiency is that with sulphur deficiency the youngest leaves are discoloured, whereas with nitrogen it is the old leaves. ▼

◄ Magnesium deficiency in potatoes, recognised by a lighter colour between the veins of older leaves and, with severe deficiency, brown leaf tips. Magnesium deficiency looks like manganese deficiency, except that with manganese deficiency symptoms are found on the young leaf.

Soil Signals

Copper

Copper deficiency mainly manifests itself in cereals. Oats suffer copper deficiency and it is often associated with peaty or very sandy soils. Besides light colouration of the leaf, dead leaf tips are also a symptom. As a result of applications of copper-rich pig manure in the past, high copper levels were often found. However, the resultant epidemic of copper poisoning in sheep is hardly ever seen nowadays.

Boron

Boron deficiency is also usually associated with sandy soils. Boron deficiency is more often found in sugar beet (heart rot), maize and lucerne. Legumes are also relatively more at risk of boron deficiency (just like molybdenum deficiency). Vegetable crops usually have lower boron requirements. Shortages are becoming less common.

Zinc

Zinc deficiency is very rare in agriculture. Maize, beans and endive are most sensitive and zinc deficiency is indicated by wide, light-coloured stripes across the leaves. In horticulture, zinc deficiency is more common, especially where soils have high phosphorus content. The newly developed shoots stop growing.

Manganese

Manganese deficiency can be recognised by a lighter colour between the veins of the leaves. It is especially visible in young leaves – in contrast to magnesium deficiency where similar symptoms are seen in older leaves. In horticulture, manganese deficiency is common in spring. Potato crops are also sensitive to manganese deficiency. Regular use of foliar sprays gives a better crop response than soil fertilisation; as pH in the soil increases, manganese availability reduces.

Silicon

Silicon deficiency is most common in cereals and grass. It leads to weak cell structures, which increases susceptibility to fungal diseases and can increase lodging risks. Although sandy soils consist predominantly of pure silicate minerals, these are not plant-available; clay soils contain the majority of minerals that release silicon in plant-available forms. Soil biota play an essential role in the release of silicon for plants.

Relationship between the availability of nutrients and soil pH

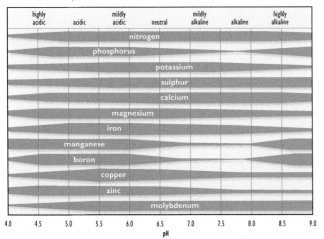

	highly acidic	acidic	mildly acidic	neutral	mildly alkaline	alkaline	highly alkaline
nitrogen							
phosphorus							
potassium							
sulphur							
calcium							
magnesium							
iron							
manganese							
boron							
copper							
zinc							
molybdenum							

pH scale: 4.0 4.5 5.0 5.5 6.0 6.5 7.0 7.5 8.0 8.5 9.0

pH

▲ *Boron deficiency occurs mainly on sandy soils and in periods of serious drought. The young leaves will discolour.*

◄ *Manganese deficiency in wheat. The light colour between veins is first observed on the young leaf.*

Organic matter

Most soils contain between 2 and 5 percent organic matter. This is made up mainly of the remains of plants and animals but around 15 percent is living organisms (soil biota). The breakdown of organic matter is a cyclical process. Part of the organic matter is transformed into carbon dioxide and water releasing energy for the soil biota; the remainder is transformed into more stable, difficult to decompose compounds (sometimes called humus).

The breakdown product depends on the carbon compounds present and the carbon to nitrogen ratio (C:N) in the organic matter. Roughly speaking, the organic matter is differentiated into three types: easily decomposable, moderately stable and very stable organic matter. Each type has its own functions within a fertile soil.

Supply and decomposition

Suppose an arable soil contains 3 percent organic matter. Annually 3 to 4 percent of the organic matter present in topsoil is decomposed. That loss has to be replenished. Organic matter from manures added and crop residues which decompose within a year supplies nutrients and feeds the soil biota. However, this quickly decomposing material may not contribute towards sustaining or increasing the organic matter content of the soil.

Cultivations improve decomposition

Soil cultivations have a negative impact on soil organic matter content. Exposing organic matter to oxygen speeds up decomposition. If organic matter is decomposed faster than it is replaced, its content is reduced in the long run. Shallow ploughing can result in higher concentrations in the topsoil as inputs of organic matter are less diluted with soil from lower layers.

▲ Crop residues from vegetables usually contain low dry matter content. They only contribute marginally to the organic matter, despite the large quantities that can remain in the field.

Mix organic matter well with the soil after you apply it. This allows soil organisms to decompose the material quickly and plant roots can access the nutrients that have been released. Do not create a surface layer of manure, but incorporate manure to a depth of about 20 cm. ▼

A cereal crop can leave a lot of residues behind. These residues become a carbon rich source of organic matter for the soil. ▼

Soil Signals

High C:N ratio

Fresh materials with a high amount of carbon relative to nitrogen (C:N ratio > 30) may temporarily lock up nitrogen after field application. For example, straw usually has a high C:N ratio. Organic matter like chicken manure, green manures and slurry with a lower C:N ratio decomposes rapidly. The application of nitrogen-rich slurry together with carbon-rich straw can allow the decomposing straw to tie up some nitrogen in organic matter. Organic matter with a relatively high C:N ratio, such as root remnants of grain and grass, remains in the soil for a long time. Composting lowers the C:N ratio of the initial materials because carbon breaks down and is lost as carbon dioxide. The carbon remaining becomes more stable due to the composting process – the more readily decomposable parts have already been lost.

Better soil structure

Plant roots have a positive effect on soil structure. Roots penetrate soils and open up cracks. Plant roots are then decomposed in the soil, adding to organic matter. Air and water movement in the soil is improved by the root channels that remain. Hence including strong and deep rooting crops can help improve soil structure. These can include green manures or crops such as grains and grasses.

Properties of organic matter types

Easily decomposed

- Supplies plant nutrients quickly.
- Sustains the soil biota.
- Improves soil structure as a result of the gums / mucus produced during its decomposition.
- Where large amounts of rapidly decomposing material is mixed into compacted soil, there is a chance of oxygen being used up.

Moderately stable

- Constant nutrient supply for soil biota and plant throughout the growing season.
- Can support a diverse soil biota.
- Improves soil structure as this type binds with mineral particles, especially clay.

Very stable

- Retains moisture in small pores.
- Attracts nutrients to its surface, especially potassium and trace elements.
- Improves soil structure through the formation of very stable micro-aggregates in which stable organic matter is bound with mineral particles.

◄ The water-holding capacity of the soil can be increased by the addition of organic matter. Sand and silt particles are like pebbles, whereas organic matter acts more like a sponge. One litre of humus can absorb 500 ml of water. However, part of the water is held in very small pores and is not available to the plant.

Aeration

Plants need accessible nutrients together with sufficient air and water in the soil. In a compacted soil, crop growth is soon restricted. If this is only localised, as in a tramline or on the headland, then it is noticeable. If the whole field does not have optimal structure, this is more difficult to detect.

A stable soil structure will give you better results than an unstable soil structure. In the latter case, soil may slump at the surface after a heavy rain storm and capping may result. If the soil is compacted, movement of air in the soil is restricted, and the roots receive insufficient oxygen and therefore take up less nutrients.

Aggregates

Soil particles and organic matter that form a stable structure unit are called aggregates or peds. The development of aggregates depends on the coagulating materials of the soil biota: when soil biota decompose organic matter, they produce gums which stick soil particles together. Earthworms ingest soil and organic matter. This is mixed in the worm with their mucus which coagulates it.

After application of organic material, fungi form long threads (hyphae) which run through the soil and can grasp and bind soil particles.

The not yet decomposed root material can temporarily strengthen the soil structure. Clay and humus provide stability to the structure through so-called clay-humus complexes. The stability is improved when the soil contains more calcium and less magnesium, potassium and sodium.

▲ Pick up a magnifying glass and evaluate the influence of the soil biota on the soil structure. Both the pores and fungal threads become visible.

The subangular blocky aggregates of this soil form a beneficial structure. Air and heat infiltrate easily, and water is retained in the small pores inside the aggregates and drains in the large pores around the outside. ▶

These angular aggregates have no visible roots. This may indicate a badly compacted soil structure. In a stable soil structure minerals and organic particles are strongly bound with pores intermixed. ▼

▲ *A subsoiler leg has loosened the soil and put oxygen in it. Rooting around it has significantly increased.*

Oxygen

Oxygen is required in the soil for root metabolism. Released carbon dioxide will have to be removed from the area around the root. It is not only the oxygen content of the soil that is important, but also the speed with which it is supplied. This is only possible if the pores in the soil are connected to the atmosphere. Therefore you should aim to achieve a soil with a crumbly structure and sufficiently high organic matter. Aerate slump-sensitive soils regularly. Soils with less water and more air heat up more quickly in the spring. This is important to start mineralisation.

Conserved green manure after one year. In this case the green manure is positioned too deeply and in anaerobic conditions. The result is rotten! ▼

What is happening here?

The blue colours around the manure particles indicate oxygen deficiency. The remnants of the manure are rotting away without benefiting the crop.

This Imants aerator is usually used on sports fields; in experiments it also provides good results on grassland. The aerator breaks the compacted soil and allows air to penetrate the soil. The root depth is increased and the compaction disappears.

Rooting

Roots need to take up water and nutrients and require energy to do so. The roots obtain this energy in the form of sugars from photosynthesis in the above ground parts of the plant. Oxygen, which is important for metabolism, has to be provided through the soil. Roots excrete root saps (exudates). These saps contain carbohydrates, proteins and sugar and form a layer around the roots where soil biota and bacteria can gain energy.

▲ *An onion has fat, shallow roots which need large pores.*

Growth space

The pores in the soil allow the roots space to grow. Some plant roots (sunflower, flax, clover) require pores of 0.3 to 0.5 mm. Other crops (onions and leeks) have thicker roots and need larger pores. Roots can penetrate small pores (0.2 mm) and expand them. As a result, pressure of between 5 and 24 bar can occur. At the point where the root thickens, rings can often be seen, indicating that the root has encountered soil resistance. A soil requires sufficient pores, otherwise roots will not grow. The soil biota contribute to the formation of soil pores, which is why you will find root hairs in worm channels. Roots are unable to penetrate compacted layers. When the compacted layer cracks due to dry conditions, the roots will take advantage of these features.

Grass roots are dense and produce a lot of organic matter - for the livestock farmer the foundation of soil fertility, and for the arable and vegetable farmer a useful soil improver. ▼

Soil structure determines root growth

Soil structure with low porosity, so low or no root growth. ▼

Soil structure with many pores. Here the roots are not restricted in their growth. ▼

Moisture and nutrients

As the soil dries out, the uptake of moisture and nutrients becomes more difficult. Nitrogen, phosphorus and pH status have a large influence on root development. When there is more nitrogen, phosphorus and lime present in the subsoil, the plant roots tend to grow towards it.

This explains why good soils are also usually deep rooted and therefore less likely to leach. Due to shortages of nutrients, plants can deal with nutrient and water shortages in the topsoil by exploring the subsoil.

▲ Wheat has a dense root system that expands width-wise along the surface and subsequently explores deeper layers.

Sugar beet has two root groups: more surface-based from the beet and more subsoil-directed from the root. ▼

A compacted layer restricts the development of roots. The sugar beet on the left are in last year's harvest tramline. The sugar beet on the right are alongside the tramline. ▼

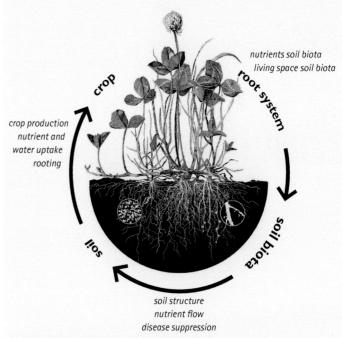

crop

nutrients soil biota
living space soil biota

root system

crop production
nutrient and
water uptake
rooting

soil biota

soil

soil structure
nutrient flow
disease suppression

Roots make the soil

Crops, rooting, soil biota and soil together form a cycle. Roots grow and die away. This continual process produces organic matter. The soil biota release nutrients for plant growth and make the space for roots to grow into. In a good grass sward up to 4500kg per hectare per year of root mass can be produced. However, this is not all stable organic matter.

Every crop has its own type of root system which makes its own demands on the soil. Cereals and grasses have root systems with many small rootlets which grow abundantly in the soil. Thus the crops contribute to the fertility of the soil. Other crops like onions, potatoes and spinach have relatively small root systems, so they contribute less to building up soil structure. The root systems of some crops, like lucerne, penetrate deeply into the soil. The swelling of their roots greatly improves the structure and accessibility of the subsoil.

Trafficability

The trafficability or carrying capacity of soil is determined by the density of the soil, the moisture content and the type of crop, e.g. grass sward. With a high water table the trafficability of soil is reduced. An old, dense sward has higher trafficability than a young reseed. The carrying capacity can be reduced noticeably with high clover content. If the topsoil shows tramlining or reshaping after trafficking, this indicates marginal trafficability.

Ideal soil structure may not always provide optimal trafficability. A soil which contains high organic matter and many pores can easily be compacted by being driven over. A good soil structure has reduced density which reduces the trafficability.

Careful planning of cultivations

Avoid traffic in the early spring and in the late autumn. At these times the soils are wet and the trafficability is limited. In the spring, land work is often carried out too early. In the autumn the topsoil may still be wet, but the subsoil may be able to withstand a lot.

Choose your heavy machinery to match your soil type

As machines have become heavier, there is increased pressure on soil. This requires good trafficability. The maximum tyre pressure is usually 0.8 bar through the season and 0.4 bar in the spring. Large trailers (e.g. grain, silage or manure trailers) exert high pressure on the soil.

If working with fixed tramlines, the soil structure in the area between the tramlines is protected. At the same time you generate better trafficability on the tramlines. This gives better traction and requires less energy. The crop development between the tramlines improves considerably, especially with fast growing crops like spinach, soon achieving an extra 5% improvement in yield. ▶

Levelling avoids puddling in low-lying areas. If the topsoil has been heavily damaged, surface drainage (digging gullies) is a better technique. ▼

Soil Signals

Improving the carrying capacity

- Ensure a deeper water table throughout the growing season.
- Create a denser sward. Grazing causes the grass to tiller, resulting in a denser sward. Set stocking has a greater effect than paddock grazing.
- Reduce the organic matter of any peaty top layer (especially with a low water table) to less than 8 percent through deep ploughing, subsoiling and the application of sand.

The plough depth should be one and a half times the depth of the humus or peaty layer. Prepare application of sand and deep ploughing very carefully in each situation because mistakes are easily made.

▲ Rubber tracks increase the area of contact with the soil and decrease the pressure on the soil.

Can you dig it?

Can you harvest after rain?

Following rain when the topsoil is too wet to carry on harvesting, the subsoil can still be dry. If you wait, it is very likely that the subsoil will also become too wet to carry machinery without damaging the soils. This is a dilemma. Soil condition during and immediately after harvest has consequences well into the next year. Avoid puddle formation after the harvest by subsoiling the ruts left by harvest machinery immediately after the harvest, so the soil can recover. Where there is standing water, there is no oxygen and the soil processes will slow down. On slopes or under conditions where the subsoil is already wet it is better to leave the surface rough, to avoid runoff and pollution of water sources.

The soil lowers with the ditch

The carrying capacity of peaty soils is often lower than is desired. Lowering the water table is not a solution because the resulting mineralisation of the peat lowers the soil even further. On deeper peat soils, sand can be applied. A sand layer of 7–10 cm can improve the carrying capacity considerably.

Chapter 3

Soil biota

Below ground the soil is teeming with life. The amount and type of soil biota present depend on the soil type and soil management. The soil biota have many positive effects as well as causing diseases and pest infestations. It is an art to get a healthy balance in the soil.

▲ *Under one hectare of pasture the soil biota are equivalent to the weight of seven cows.*

Soil biota are dependent on both soil management and soil type. Experience shows that permanent grassland contains many varied worms. However, after growing maize for several years in the same soil, there may be no worms left. In young, high calcium clay soils there are many bacteria which are able to decompose organic matter very rapidly. Fungi carry out some useful work in forestry soils and acid sand soils. They also turn organic matter into humus.

The many different organisms are part of a food chain. Motto: eat or be eaten. The soil is not evenly 'densely populated'. You encounter concentrations of soil biota in specific places. Around roots many organisms are active due to the exudation of root sap and the death of root cells. The nutrient- and oxygen-rich tunnels made by roots or worms and crumbly soil particles close to the surface both sustain a high concentration of soil biota. Similarly high numbers of soil biota are found in grass swards and where green or regular manure has been incorporated.

Soil
Signals

Utilising soil biota

The soil biota ensures the foundation of a good soil structure by:

- loosening compacted soils by digging tunnels.
- mixing and transporting organic matter and soil particles.
- building soil pores.

Encourage active and diverse soil biota by:

- fertilising with farmyard manures.
- encouraging an active root system.
- keeping soil covered.
- working with green manures.

Soil biota is disadvantaged by:

- fallow soils.
- a cropping plan without grass and cereals.
- no import of (fresh) organic matter.
- intensive cultivations.
- compaction of the soil.
- poor drainage.
- drought.

The recyclers

The soil biota decompose organic material. Breakdown products are derived from this decomposition; these in turn act as nutrients to other soil organisms or become available as water soluble feedstocks (nutrients) for the plant. The food chain of decomposition has three main levels:

Predatory nematodes, predatory mites and some types of springtails eat fungus and bacteria-eating nematodes and springtails.

predatory nematodes   *predatory mites*

Independently of this food chain, organic matter is also directly digested by worms.

Fungal and bacteria-eating nematodes (eelworms) and springtails feast on micro-organisms.

   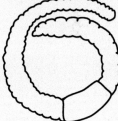

bacteria-eating nematodes   *fungus eating nematodes*   *springtails*

Micro-organisms like bacteria and fungi consume dead organic matter.

Earthworms and pot worms

Many soil organisms are not visible with the naked eye or even a magnifying glass. However, earthworms are easily seen. They are 3.5 to 16 cm long. Pot worms are much smaller than earthworms. They measure between 0.5 to 4 cm and are white in colour. Active worms in the soil are a sign of good cycling of organic matter.

Moisture and nutrients for earthworms

A moist soil is important for worms. When the soil dries out the worm will move deeper into the soil layers and transform to a resting state or die. As well as moisture, they have to find food. Include crops with large residues in your rotation and use manure and compost. Sufficient air in the soil is also important. Take care with intense cultivations; worms quickly become casualties.

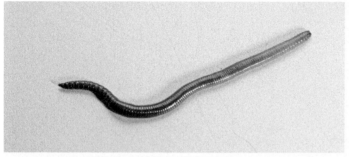

The most abundant litter-dwelling worm is the red earthworm (Lumbricus rubellus). These red worms, lighter in colour on the underside, live close to the soil surface and are frequently found under dung pads. They are usually very active. These worms decompose plant residues and manure, but because of their location at the surface, they contribute less to the development of soil structure.

Burrowing worms can be distinguished from the soil dwellers as they are lighter in colour on the lower side (Lumbricus terrestris and the grey Aporrectodea longa). They are active worms and they eat plant remains that lie on the soil surface, drawing them downwards into their vertical tunnels. These burrows are an important route for air penetration, especially in clay soils. In all soils they are an important route for water infiltration, allowing water to move through the topsoil (without leaching nutrients) and reach the roots in the subsoil. Note the flat tail.

Soil dwelling worms include the grey worm (Aporrectodea caliginosa). These worms are the same grey colour on the upper and lower surfaces, and will remain motionless on your hand. Soil dwelling worms move through the soil and move large amounts of soil, creating large pores, which is good for soil structure. In western Europe these are the most common worm.

Enchytraeid worms (pot worms) are much smaller than earthworms and are soil dwelling. They decompose any organic materials within the soil (soil organic matter, manure, compost and plant residues) and help to form stable organic matter.

Nematodes

Nematodes (eelworms) are the nightmare of many a farmer and gardener – at least as far as the plant parasitic species are concerned. But in fact there are a range of nematode types and many have useful functions. These nematodes eat other soil organisms and regulate the number of bacteria and fungi. In this process nutrients can be released.

Some nematodes suppress soil diseases. Carnivorous nematodes can be used to control fungi. The product Nemaslug contains parasitic nematodes which infects slugs with bacteria that in turn kill the slugs.

Types of nematodes

Different nematode types feed on different organisms including bacteria, fungi, the living parts of plant roots and other soil animals. The following types are differentiated according to their most important food source:

- Plant eaters
- Bacteria eaters
- Fungi eaters
- Predatory nematodes - feed on other nematodes and protozoa
- Omnivores – eat a variety of organisms or have a different diet at each development stage.

Take a close look at the nematodes

Nematodes can be differentiated by the shape of their mouth. Of the nematodes pictured the one on the left eats dead plants and bacteria. The middle one is the parasitic type: it sucks sap from plants and can spread viruses. The one on the right is a parasitic nematode that eats other soil organisms.

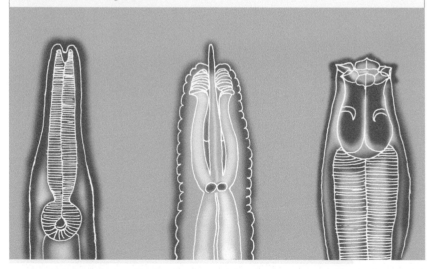

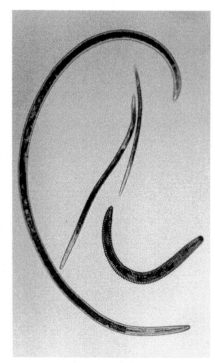

◄ Nematodes or eelworms are small worms (0.2 – 2 mm long) which are present in large quantities and many types. As the name suggests, they look like miniature eels.

Bacteria and fungi

Bacteria

Bacteria are single-celled organisms. Despite their small size they contribute the largest biomass to the soil biota. Bacteria feed on soil organic matter. They subsequently fall prey to different hunters which are positioned higher up in the food chain and this releases nutrients.

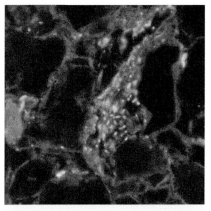

The mucus produced during decomposition of organic matter by bacteria binds soil particles. This can help create greater water retention in the soil.

Some bacteria can break down organic matter even when oxygen is not present. Products from this process can stain the soil. For example, the blue colouration of clay soil is caused by compounds in which reduced iron plays a role. ▼

Fungal hyphae

Fungi form threads which grow in between soil particles. In contrast to bacteria, fungi are able to decompose carbon rich organic matter. They absorb the products released by the decomposing materials, preventing them from being leached. Some fungi can break down lignin (the woody part of the cell walls). This process produces lignin-stable humus. Therefore, take care of fungi.

pH and aeration

Fungi are active in an acid (low pH) soil and in these soils organic matter accumulates. Liming to achieve high pH stimulates bacterial activity. This breaks down organic matter and releases more nutrients for the crop. An aerated soil is a prerequisite for the growth of fungi. This is the opposite to the requirements for bacteria. A significant number for bacteria can live more or less without oxygen. These anaerobic bacteria use other nutrients as chemicals in the oxidation process. For example, denitrifying bacteria use nitrate to help them breathe; this releases nitrogen which is lost to the plant. This happens in grassland after applications of artificial fertiliser followed by a wet period.

Fungi and their threads bind the soil particles together and thereby improve the soil structure. Fungi are able to form long threads, as evidenced by fairy rings, the flowering method of a single fungal organism. Fairy rings can be anything up to 880 ha in size.

Ratio of fungi to bacteria

Some gardeners are paying more attention to the fungal to bacterial ratio in the soil. Every crop grows best with a fungal to bacterial ratio that is related to its natural state. For example, the wild strawberry grows along forest edges alongside fungi, so it will grow best on agricultural soils dominated by fungi. Annual crops and grasses prefer a more bacterial dominant soil.

Mycorrhizal fungi

Mycorrhizal fungi form a symbiotic relationship with plants. In exchange for energy (sugars) from the plants, fungi benefit them. With their hyphae they extend the rooting ability of the plant and the plant is better able to take up water and nutrients (like phosphate), improve soil structure and become disease resistant.

Mycorrhizal fungi are naturally present in most soils. The diversity and extent of fungal colonisation on plant roots is dependent on soil fertility and fertilisation levels. Generally these fungi prefer low fertility levels and a hungry soil, for example sand. This is logical, as the plant will only work with the fungi if there is something in it for the plant, for example nutrients. But the relationship costs the plant something too – sugars that the plant provides to the fungi.

Can you dig it?

Spot the difference!

The onions on the left have been treated with mycorrhizal fungi, while those on the right haven't. The possible effect of treatment with mycorrhizal fungi is greatest for plants with poor root development. It appears from pot experiments that onion yield can be improved by 50 percent. The results from field experiments are less spectacular, but point towards a better onion yield.

Characteristic structure (arbuscle) of mycorrhizal fungi in a clover root. ▼

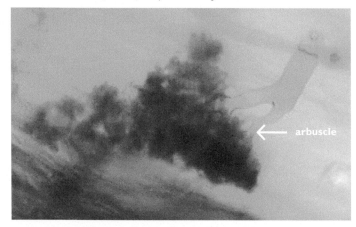

← arbuscle

▲ *Compost increases disease resistance.*

Where potatoes are in a 1 in 3 year rotation, the yield is reduced. Problems are associated with soil-borne diseases such as nematodes, verticillium, potato scab, powdery scab and rhizoctonia. ▼

Soil diseases and plagues

Diseases associated with the soil are rare in natural ecosystems. In agricultural systems, however, these diseases can cause persistent problems. Infections often appear due to cultivating a crop too intensively. Other causes are the importation of infected plant material from outside the business, or situations such as soil on a harvester belonging to contractors. With the increase in sugar beet harvesting and contracting the spread of rhizomania has increased markedly.

Prevention is better than cure

- **Frequency of cropping (rotational cropping)**
  To avoid soil-borne diseases it is advisable for most susceptible crops to have a crop rotation of one in six years. There is a large difference between crops. You can grow cereal rye in successive years without any problems, whilst peas can even suffer problems when grown only once every six years.

- **Closed system**
  Importing plant materials, soil or contracting carries infection risk. By using your own plant material (for example stem cuttings of potatoes) and using your own machinery you can reduce the risk.

- **Biosecurity**
  Only accept cleaned contractors' machinery. Use certified seeds and planting stocks. Ensure that any imports contain as little soil as possible.

- **Soil analysis**
  Only through regular analysis of the soil for indicators of soil-borne diseases can focused management decisions be taken and the best crop rotation and good use of green manures identified.

Each soil-borne disease needs to be dealt with on an individual basis. Clubroot in brassica crops is avoided by increasing soil pH.

Rhizomania in sugar beet is controlled to a reasonable level by choosing resistant varieties.

Controlling nematodes on light sand soils and in greenhouses is less easy. Here a more integrated approach needs to be carried out, consisting of biosecurity management, choice of resistant varieties and when necessary soil sterilisation with chemicals, steam or water. This destroys everything within the treated depth of soil, thus also destroying beneficial soil organisms. Following sterilisation soil biota need to re-establish. The danger is that only the disease-causing organisms will develop, giving a lop-sided unbalanced community of soil biota. Once you start with sterilisation, a programme of continually repeated treatment is usually required. That is why an integrated approach is carried out more often than full scale field sterilisation. For each situation, the best fit strategy needs to be carefully considered.

▲ *Sticky nightshade is a good destroyer of the potato cyst nematode.*

Marigolds are a good destroyer of the stubby root nematode, while at the same time encouraging other beneficial nematodes such as Trichodoridae. ▼

Biological nematode control

If you encourage and feed soil biota, you can count on a rich diversity of soil organisms. Those that cause disease are then less able to dominate as they are controlled by their natural predators. The damage to the crop remains limited. A supply of organic matter in the shape of crop residues, farmyard manures and compost feed soil biota. With a healthy cropping plan you can further increase the disease resistance of the soil.

Oilseed radish varieties with a high resistance to beet cyst nematode (BCS 1) are able to reduce the eelworm population by 90 percent in a rotation. This is less effective in a stubble rotation, depending on the timing of planting, soil temperature and moisture content. Varieties with insufficient resistance can actually increase the pest population. ▼

Chapter 4

Evaluating soils

▲ Soil composition can be assessed well in the laboratory.

The evaluation of soil characteristics is necessary in order to understand the growth of the crop. One approach is to use soil chemical analysis. Alongside chemical analysis, it is useful to evaluate the soil in the field in order to understand soil structure and its interaction with rooting which mediates the uptake of nutrients from the soil.

of fertiliser. However, you may want to establish first how much nitrogen is supplied via the soil.

Good growth

Even if a crop is growing well, there can be a nutrient imbalance or over-supply of phosphate, potassium and magnesium. It may be necessary to adjust the application of fertilisers in order to bring this back in line. If pH is too high, reduce liming rates. Lodging due to high nitrogen? Check the soil organic matter and the nitrogen availability. Excessive fertilisation costs money, reduces product quality and can contravene environmental laws.

Soil analysis

Soil chemical analysis is a useful tool for deciding upon appropriate fertiliser application. When a crop does not grow well, you can take a soil sample and you will often be able to identify the growth-limiting factor via the analysis. Even in a crop that is growing well, soil analysis helps to fine tune the application of fertiliser.

Poor growth

With poor growth, a soil analysis is particularly important. Nitrogen and phosphorus are partly supplied from the breakdown of organic matter and application of fertiliser. Where possible, increase the supply of nutrients through decomposition of organic matter and in the meantime top up with applications

Soil
Signals

Types of soil analysis

There are many laboratories capable of undertaking soil analyses. Soil reaction (pH), available nutrients and organic matter are nearly always determined. In some laboratories additional analyses are carried out to provide more information on aspects such as soil mineral nitrogen supply capacity, organic matter quality and soil biota.

How often should you analyse your soil?

Some farms carry out a basic soil analysis every year while on others there may be a ten year interval. Both of these sampling frequencies can be the right choice. Dairy farms that make use of derogations are required to have an analysis report of each field that is no more than four years old. Analysis is necessary with:

- poor understanding of the soil or crop to be planted.
- poor soil fertility.
- high yielding crops. Crops that require large quantities of nitrogen and potassium must be monitored more closely.
- sandy soils. With sand, the pH can quickly drop and nutrients are leached (especially nitrogen and potassium). Analysis will be needed in sandy soils more often than loams or clay soils.
- reseeding grassland.

Sampling method

Take 40 subsamples per field and mix them together to give one (or a small number of) sample(s) for analysis. Only with very homogenous areas should this quantity be reduced. With grass the top 10-15 cm should be sampled. In arable soils sample to the working depth of at least 20 cm but no deeper than 30 cm. So that results can be compared over several years it is important to keep sampling to exactly the same depth each time.

Soil sampling for a chemical soil analysis in an arable field.

Soil sampling for a chemical soil analysis in a grass field.

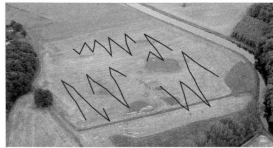

Sampling method

If a field is not homogenous as a result of soil differences and variations seen in previous cropping, sample each section separately. Avoid any uncharacteristic parts of the field if they are small, e.g. the wet areas within the field shown. Do not mix different soil types in the same sample. Walk in a criss-cross pattern when sampling such as that indicated by the red line.

Evaluation of chemical analysis

Chemical analysis is important for the design of a good fertiliser strategy. But how do you interpret the results?

Advice basis for fertilising

Considerable research and development in soil science enables the delivery of appropriate fertiliser recommendations based on the results of soil analysis.

The conclusions derived from a soil analysis always have to relate to the farmer's experience in the field in the past and to the soil quality which is evaluated on the spot. ▶

Arable soil analysis

■ Organic matter content

It is not always achievable, especially in sandy soils, though maintaining organic matter at three percent is advisable. The target should be somewhat higher in heavy soils. Watch out: if organic matter gets too high, workability and weed problems increase.

■ pH

A fertile calcium-supplying soil usually has a pH between 6 and 7. In calcium-poor soils the pH can become too low. The speed at which this happens depends very much on the soil texture, crop and fertiliser. Adjust the sampling frequency accordingly.

■ Availability of phosphorus and potassium

The concentration of phosphorus and potassium can become too low, because crops extract much of these nutrients from the soils. Very high concentrations due to imprecise fertilisation also occur.

■ The soil nitrogen supply

The soil mineral nitrogen supply can be estimated with the aid of total nitrogen and the C:N ratio in the soil. In the field the weather and soil structure also play a part in determining nitrogen supply. Take this into account when choosing the fertiliser rate.

Additional supply

During routine soil analysis, only plant-available nutrients are determined. There are also additional supplies from the total nutrient reserve within the soil. This is the case with nitrogen in high organic matter soils. On peaty soils this can be in the order of several hundreds of kilograms per hectare. Young sea clays supply lots of potassium but are often low in phosphate. Sandy soils often have relatively low total nutrient reserves, but when manures in the past have supplied more nutrients than the crop has needed, these soils can have high phosphate concentrations and subsequently high phosphorus additional supply.

Grassland soil analysis

- Organic matter content

This is an indicator of soil quality, but just as in arable soils, it is also needed to calculate the fertiliser potassium and lime additions required. On grassland an organic matter content of 5 to 6 percent is advisable in the 0-10 cm layer. Reseeding operations usually reduce the organic matter content – so you should only do this if it is absolutely necessary.

- pH

With the reduction of slurry applications over the last few years, the acidifying effect is reduced and liming is required less often. The correct pH value is essential for nutrient management and soil biota. On sandy soils the value should not be below 5.0 or above 6.0.

- Availability of phosphorus and potassium

On many sandy grassland soils an excess of manure has been applied in the past and this can still be seen by the high available phosphorus levels. Phosphorus is an important nutrient for grass, but if there are high soil levels, its application should be restricted. On sandy soils large quantities of potassium can be leached and low potassium concentrations exist. Equally, where a lot of potassium has been applied as fertiliser or in manure, extremely high concentrations can be found. It is important to establish the potassium supply from manures and compare this with the supply in the soil.

- The soil nitrogen supply

From the total soil nitrogen content and the C:N ratio, the soil mineral nitrogen supply can be estimated. On grassland soil mineral nitrogen supply often makes up a large proportion of the nitrogen supply. Take this specifically into account when evaluating the annual nitrogen requirement and the fertiliser requirement of individual cuts. The soil mineral nitrogen supply is also dependent on the soil structure, the moisture content and the temperature. A subsequent field evaluation is recommended.

Example of a grassland soil analysis. ▼

Evaluation in the field

An effective way to evaluate the condition and quality of the soil is to dig a small pit in the field with a spade. Within a pit, you can evaluate indicators of soil structure, rooting by the crop and soil biota activity. Investigation of a soil pit and chemical soil analysis complement each other.

It is worth the effort to examine fields over time and to compare fields that have had different cultivations, types of organic matter applied (e.g. farmyard manure or slurry), permanent and reseeded grassland and whether clover is or is not included in the sward. This way you can observe any effect of changes in management and define your own reference points for good and bad soil quality that can help lead to an improvement in management.

When to dig a soil pit

Evaluation of soil in a pit can be done at any time during the year. However, you can see the structure of the soil better when the soil is reasonably moist. It is also easier on heavy soils to dig a pit if the soil is still moist. When a crop is present in the field, a pit will allow you to see close up how it roots through the soil.

Dig a pit to expose a 50 x 50 cm face of soil (profile), preferably between the crop rows and within a representative area in the field.

Scrape the walls of the pit gently with a knife and feel for the differences in the soil structure.

Crop roots will also become easily visible as you scrape the soil loose from the face of the pit with a knife.

Soil Signals

Location

There will be natural variation in soils which can be seen in differences between soil profiles within short distances. However, one well chosen pit is usually adequate. It is important to select the location of the pit in such a way that it is representative of the majority of the field. Insight can be provided into specific queries by a comparison between two pits, for example comparing areas where crop growth is very different.

To dig a useful soil pit...

- Dig a minimum of 10 metres away from the field edge.
- Pay attention to the soil surface and slope in the field and avoid non-representative areas.
- Carefully observe the crop growth; does the colour and stand of the crop give an indication about the soil?
- Avoid tramlines: underneath tramlines compacted soil is usually present.
- Dig a pit with a spade to expose a face/profile of soil that is about 50 cm wide and at least 50 cm deep.
- Evaluate the rooting, the structure, the activity of soil biota and the colour of the soil by scraping the soil with a knife along the pit wall.

▲ *In this humus-rich soil, very dense and deep rooting of the crop can be seen.*

In grassland a spade in the soil can deliver a lot of information. The rooting tells a story about the soil condition. Shallow rooting occurs in grassland with poor structure and in grassland where a lot of mineral fertilisers are used (lazy crop). This makes the crop drought prone and nutrient deficient. Deeper rooting is possible with a good soil structure. So always cultivate a little deeper than the roots; by observation you can see where the limiting factor in the subsoil is.

The sudden change from humus-rich topsoil onto a white sand soil indicates poor biological activity in this podzolic soil. Biological activity would mix these layers together. ▶

Collecting an undisturbed soil profile

With a large cylindrical cutter an undisturbed column of soil can be cut to a depth of 40 cm. After the column is removed from the cutter it can be kept without drying out in a PVC pipe or it can be examined immediately. When the column is split into two lengthways, the layers can be examined. Root development is easily visible, and because a fixed area is cut, root density can be established.

Soil layers

Soil layers tell us a lot about the soil processes and the history of the soil. The various layers in the soil differ in colour, thickness, density, pore content and root growth. Soil layers tell us something about:

- supply and breakdown of organic matter.
- leaching, infiltration and homogenisation (mixing).
- oxidation and reduction (reacting with oxygen or in absence of oxygen).
- soil cultivations and their effects.

Humus-rich topsoil

Crop remnants and roots form a dark, humus-rich topsoil layer. Cultivations mix the layers together. Hence the depth of the humus enriched layer gives an indicator of depth of soil cultivations, both past and present. If the roots in this layer are restricted, then this will have direct consequences on the availability of nutrients to the crop.

Organic matter or iron and aluminium compounds can leach in dry sandy soils and deposit themselves deeper in the soil. This manifests itself in a red layer that is sometimes compacted and impenetrable. On loamy soils the leaching of clay and iron can occur. This causes a compacted layer further down the profile.

The use of slurry over the years has caused slumping in the humus-rich topsoil above the white sand. ▼

Soil Signals

Soil colour

The colour of the soil is determined to a large extent by the colour imparted by organic matter and iron compounds. In a good soil, the homogenous coloured layers pass fluidly from one to the next. Brown or black topsoil transforms into a rather neutral to a light warm colour in the subsoil. This colour is defined by the parent material and is usually brownish, reddish or yellowish, where natural drainage is good. Greyish colours, often with rusty or ochreous mottling are indicative of waterlogging (see following section).

Distinct or garish colours: take care!

A layer showing very distinct colours in the soil can be a strong indication that there is a problem with the water management and the structure. Rust areas indicate oxidised iron compounds and fluctuating water content. This can be an indicator of the height of the water in the winter periods. This patchiness takes years to develop or can remain as a fossil relic of former wetter conditions, perhaps prior to the installation of a drainage scheme. So you can't deduce from it that the soil water table was high recently.

If you discover a blue grey colour in the soil, this indicates reduced iron compounds (ferrous) in an oxygen poor (anaerobic) environment. Poor aeration limits root growth or makes this impossible, and slows down the breakdown of manures and crop remnants. Such layers point to a shallow water table.

How would you evaluate this soil?

In the subsoil layering is clearly visible; the result of sea deposition. The rust areas in the lower layers indicate the influence of soil water. ▼

The leaching of iron can lead to a strong red colouration (or ochre) in the deep soil layer where the iron is precipitated again. Blue colouration indicates anaerobic conditions resulting from persistent waterlogging. ▼

In this soil rooting is restricted to the topsoil. This leads to very inefficient mineral utilisation, and can lead to large losses of nutrients. Reseeding grassland can change this. The incorporation of well composted organic manures can allow the roots to penetrate the soil more effectively.

Carefully dig out a soil slice by loosening the soil left and right with the spade.

Pull the clod up. Support with the hand, so that the soil slice remains in one piece.

Put the soil slice carefully on the ground.

Break up the soil slice in order to evaluate the undisturbed soil.

Evaluation of a soil slice

In order to evaluate the soil structure it is not always necessary to dig a pit. Often results can be obtained with a slice or block of soil on a spade. This method is quick and can be repeated at many places in the field.

The soil slice in ten steps

1. Dig a soil slice in one piece out of the 0 – 25 cm top layer, preferably around a plant.

2. Pull the soil slice out of the ground, supporting it well.

3. Put the soil slice on the ground or on a crate.

4. See whether you can identify different layers and measure the thickness of each layer.

5. See whether there is visible undisturbed root growth in each layer and whether it is limited, average or dense.

6. Break off or cut a smaller soil slice with a knife.

7. Assess the percentage of different types of soil aggregates in each layer of this soil slice.

8. Assess the activity of the soil biota in each layer.

9. Assess the soil colour and the extent of breakdown of crop and manure remnants in each layer.

10. You may want to repeat these steps in deeper soil layers if you can.

Soil Signals

Soil aggregates

In soil structure evaluation, the way in which soil particles (sand, silt, clay and organic matter) are clumped together plays a crucial role. There are three basic shapes of these soil aggregates that can be identified: crumbs, subangular blocky and angular blocky aggregates.

In the topsoil you will mainly find many crumbs. This can be caused by dense rooting and biological activity. In the deeper layers larger aggregates, both subangular blocky and angular blocky, are found. The distinction between the two types of structural aggregates is not always easy to define.

Loose crumbs of 0.3 to 1 cm. With crumbs roots are able to root very densely through the soils.

Subangular blocky aggregates of 1 to 10 cm. With rough treatment they can easily break down into crumbs, but it depends how they appear in the soil. Usually they contain a lot of pores and they are easily rooted.

Evaluation of soil aggregates

Type	Rating
Crumbs	Very beneficial
Subangular blocky	Beneficial
Angular blocky	Detrimental. Can impede root growth, water movement and breakdown of manure.

Angular blocky aggregates: angular, compact blocks from small to very big. Generally roots will have to grow around these, and there is only a small proportion of the soil available for roots. If there are roots present, this is usually the result of spring cultivations when the soil is loose and allows rooting. Under wet conditions angular blocky aggregates may be blue on the inside due to lack of oxygen.

Good structure

In this soil all the physical conditions for good growth are present even with a low fertiliser rate. There are also disadvantages: when cultivating with heavy machines, the carrying capacity of the soil can be inadequate.

Moderate structure

Besides angular blocky aggregates, subangular blocky aggregates and crumbs also exist. You will find these in most soils. There is space for the soil biota and roots, and air is able to penetrate the soil. But there are also some sharp blocked aggregates, so the structure can be improved.

Bad structure

Here sharp angular blocky aggregates dominate. The roots have very poor spaces. In these soil slices there is not enough oxygen present to allow good root development. Crops can only grow where there is good manuring and good management of the water supply. If possible, improve soil structure using crop choice, manuring and soil cultivations.

Evaluating structure

Arable soil structure

With arable soils particular structural aggregates are often easily recognisable when ploughing or cultivating.

Description of a reasonable to good structure in arable soils:

- At 0-25 cm depth, crumbs make up at least 25 percent of the volume of the soil. The rest consists of rootable subangular blocky aggregates. There should be no angular blocky aggregates.
- At 25-50 cm depth there is at least 25 percent of crumbs or rootable subangular blocky aggregates. The rest consists of non-rootable angular blocky aggregates.

Compare locations

The percentage of angular blocky aggregates is a useful criterion when comparing soil slices from different locations. Angular blocky aggregates are the easiest aggregates to distinguish; subangular blocky aggregates are easily confused with crumbs.

Soil cultivations can help to temporarily improve the soil structure. However, a lasting structural improvement can only be achieved through cultivations in conjunction with other measures, such as growing crops with dense and deep rooting systems.

Soil Signals

Grassland soil structure

Grassland might be compacted because of cattle and tractors on the ground. The principle of assessment is the same as on arable ground; however, the method differs when considering grassland. Collect a soil slice in the same way, but with grassland you start your assessment with the underside of the soil slice. Open up the soil with a knife. If the breaks are angular with smooth sides then this layer is made up of angular blocky aggregates, and when compacted it can form a large compacted mass without natural fissures.

Towards the surface the number of roots and worm channels often increases and the structure is increasingly made up of more subangular blocky aggregates. Usually the quantity of crumbs gradually increases towards the top. In grassland the surface layer is a dense sod with virtually only crumbs between the roots.

Put the sod upside down on your hand. Scrape with your knife ten times over the underside and repeat this again at right angles to the previous movement. Now measure the depth of the sod with a tape measure.

Measuring the thickness of the sod

Turn a dug out sod over. Firmly scrape with a knife ten times over the underside.

Repeat this at right angles.

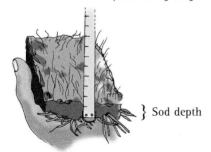

} Sod depth

Then you can measure the thickness.

Good structure

The sod is more than 5 cm thick, with predominantly crumbs and subangular blocky aggregates up to 10 cm. From 10 to 20 cm subangular blocky aggregates or crumbs make up at least 25 percent of the volume of the soil. A healthy soil.

Moderate structure

The sod is 3 to 5 cm thick. Directly underneath is a layer with subangular blocky aggregates and crumbs. Within 10 cm there is a layer that is predominantly angular blocky aggregates. This situation is not ideal, so the soil structure demands attention.

Poor structure

The sod is less than 3 cm in depth. Immediately below it a compact angular blocky structure is visible. Roots are unable to develop and struggle to penetrate this layer. Adjust the trafficking, grazing and manuring accordingly.

Rooting evaluation

In a pit and a soil slice you can see both how the roots grow and also what they encounter during their growth. There are many reasons why roots cannot develop: not enough air; compacted soil; too dry. Suboptimal growth can also mean a deficiency of nutrients. For example, in the soil water there are only a few kilograms of phosphorus per hectare, which is insufficient for good growth. In response, the root will grow towards the phosphorus in the soil, thus stimulating root development.

Criteria for assessing rooting are:

- Degree of rooting: nothing, moderate or dense rooting in the various layers.
- Root type: old roots, active roots and root hairs.
- Root infections: when present, these indicate soil-borne diseases and plagues.
- Rooting depth: the optimum depth differs from crop to crop.
- Shape of the root system: disturbed growth or kinking in the roots can indicate problems with soil structure.

When the soil is poorly rootable, the quantity of roots is reduced, the roots become thicker, strange bends occur and the number of side shoots declines. Also check whether these roots are white and active or brownish-yellow and dying back.

Rooting in the topsoil

Alongside evaluation of the root pattern in the topsoil you can count the number of roots. Do this in a pit and a given distance away from the plants, e.g. from 10 cm. If there are a lot of roots at 20 cm, this indicates that the subsoil is ideal for rooting. If there are only a few roots, this suggests that plants will only be able to use moisture and nutrients from the topsoil.

Typical rooting in a compacted soil. Roots have difficulty growing between the angular blocky clods. There is poor penetration through the soil. Availability of air and uptake of nutrients by crops becomes difficult. ▼

After digging a soil slice you can count the number of roots. ▼

Soil
Signals

Rooting in grassland

Within grassland, the sod depth is a measure of the depth of dense rooting. You can also dig out a soil slice and count the roots to evaluate rooting. It is clear that most of the roots can be found in the top 3 to 5 cm. In ideal grassland many roots are present to a depth of about 15-20 cm. Also check any herbs: if they have tap roots, they will penetrate much deeper into the soil. This applies to dandelion and also red clover. So adjust your evaluation of rooting to the type of plant. With farmland you are able to clearly identify the structural aggregates from the pattern of root growth. In grassland topsoil this is also the case, but after a few centimetres there is often a compacted mass. The roots then look for cracks or worm channels. In your soil analysis, make sure you sample all the soil between 0 and 10 cm. If the roots are restricted in the accessibility of this layer, adjust the choice of manuring. This is especially the case for phosphorus.

Rooting in the subsoil

Plants require roots deeper than the topsoil to support the uptake of water and nutrients. When soil analysis down to 50 cm is carried out, it can be surprising how high the nutrient concentration is at that depth. If roots cannot reach this, the nutrients may be leached with drainage water. Dead roots are also nutrition for soil biota; if there are no roots at great depth then there are unlikely to be significant soil biota.

Deep rooting is more important in fields where the crop is dependent on the water supply via the capillary action from the soil water table. At least 2 mm moisture per day should be supplied to overcome drought risk. The maximum distance between roots and ground water table should be:

- Sand 80 cm
- Loam 100 cm
- Clay 65 cm

Root number per 25 x 25 cm

	Low	High
At 10 cm	80	450
At 20 cm	50	300

◄ *Poor-rooting maize. Maize has a tendency to deeply penetrate the soil with its roots. When the soil is compacted this is not possible. Poor growth is the result.*

Can you dig it?

What do these roots indicate?

There are soil particles stuck to the roots. This indicates dense contact with the soil. From the crumb structure you can deduce that air and oxygen are available to the roots. This crumb structure is an ideal environment for good root development.

▲ Compost has been applied to compacted clay soil. When feeding on the compost the earthworms also loosen the compacted soil.

Evaluation of soil biota

Part of the soil biota is visible, part is not. The beneficial effects of soil biota can be readily seen. Indicators of good activity of soil biota are:

- a good rooting ability of the soil.
- the development of good soil structure.
- a good breakdown of manures and plant remnants.
- an open structure with a large proportion of air spaces to supply oxygen and provide easy access for roots.

Earthworms

The most visible are the earthworms. The red ones digest the fresh material, the grey ones work on the structure of the soil and the soil-dwelling species make the subsoil accessible to air and roots and improve drainage. Because the worm types have different functions it is important that all three are present.

The quantity of worms varies throughout the year. In late summer and autumn they are numerous. In addition, the moisture content of the soil is important; a long dry period delays worm development.

An earthworm makes a tunnel in the compacted soil. After this, plant roots are able to reach the subsoil more easily. ▼

Quantity of adult worms per m² to a depth of 25 cm

	Low	High
Arable	25	75
Grassland	50	150

Classification of worm types

	Colour	Movement	Depth (cm)	Feed source	Main function
Epigeic species (litter species)	Red	Fast	0-20	Plant remnants and organic matter	Breakdown of organic matter
Endogeic species (subsoil species)	Grey	Slow	0-40	Organic matter	Structural improvement
Anecic species (soil-dwelling species)	Red/pink	Moderate	0-300	Plant remnants	Aeration

Soil Signals

Not directly visible soil biota

Not visible, but no less important. Nematodes, bacteria, fungi and many other organisms are essential for important soil processes. Several laboratories offer analysis that can provide information such as the structure of the soil food web, the mineralisation of nitrogen, and the carbon dioxide production from soil biota.

The practical interpretation of the results of soil biological analysis is still in its infancy. However, the role of soil biota in the delivery of soil functions is currently a very important focus of research.

▲ *Worm counting helps us better understand the activity of soil biota.*

Too many soil biota

Following many wet years recently in the Netherlands, especially in the Flevopolders, the excessive numbers of earthworms have been causing problems. With the use of heavy machines, in combination with readily available potato and sugar beet foliage, there are sometimes more than 500 worms per square metre in compacted soil. This is resulting in undesired soil structure. Under normal circumstances this worm density would actually be beneficial. Field evidence suggested that the use of burned lime (5 t/ha) or gypsum (10 t/ha) may help reduce the structural problems caused by too many worms. However, it has not been possible to give well-founded advice based on the soil analysis.

With clover there are twice as many worms present as with grass. With clover you can stimulate the soil biota activity in a dead soil very well. ▼

Loose soil caused by worm activity. ▼

Earthworm passages are often clearly visible at a depth of 20 cm in grassland. If you encounter more than ten in an area of 25 x 25 cm, that is a lot. ▼

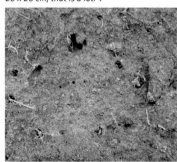

Chapter 5

Soil cultivations

Soil cultivations help to prepare the soil and make it optimal for crop germination and growth. By repeatedly cultivating the topsoil you make it homogeneous to the working depth and more accessible for root development. However, cultivations can also have an adverse effect, if they destroy or weaken existing structure and lead to slumping of the soil. The most common errors are cultivating too deep, with too much power or too often. As a general rule: do no more than is strictly necessary.

▲ *The practice of ploughing is centuries old but is still being developed.*

Soil cultivations can be subdivided into:
- spring cultivations: for seed and planting bed preparation.
- autumn cultivations: stubble cultivations and subsoiling, weeding, and creating a seed bed for green manures or winter crops like cererals. Cultivations are also needed to incorporate green manures, crop remnants and organic manures.
- main cultivations: ploughing or digging.

Ploughing

Through the turning action of the plough, crop remnants and weed seeds are buried. 'Clean' soil is brought to the surface. The furrow slice is exposed to weathering if the land is left fallow over winter; this is particularly useful in clay soils. If all the organic matter from crop remnants, green manures and organic manures remains in the top 10 to 15 cm of soil, the organic matter level in this layer will rise more quickly. In the long term this ensures a good soil condition. For most conditions, the benefits of ploughing deeper than 20 to 25 cm have never been proven. Farmers also tend to plough deeper than they think, on average by about 5 cm.

During ploughing, the furrow in which the tractor drives is the most vulnerable part of the soil. The loading on the wheel that travels in the furrow is higher due to the tilting angle of the tractor. Compaction of the subsoil is increasingly found to be due to ploughing and other cultivations. The use of wide tyres with low pressure can provide a technical solution but the problem with most ploughing operations is that the small furrow provides insufficient space for a wide tyre.

In order to drive with wide tyres and low pressure there are two possibilities:

1. Driving with wheels on the top rather than in the furrow.
2. Ploughing a wide furrow with good turning action and not too deep.

Shallow ploughing

Shallow ploughing at 15 to 20 cm has its advantages. Organic materials such as crop remnants, green manures and organic manures stay in the topsoil, where there is plenty of oxygen to help break them down. For the crops, this ensures that minerals from the organic matter are used more effectively. By increasing the organic matter content in the topsoil both the water holding capacity and aggregate stability are usually increased and slump-sensitive soils become more stable. However, not every soil is completely suited to shallow ploughing. Soils with weak aggregate stability which naturally compress easily may need to be regularly cultivated more deeply.

◀ Two-layer plough mouldboard. With this plough it is possible to achieve both shallow ploughing and deep loosening at the same time. The top shear turns the shallow furrow. The smaller lower shear loosens the subsoil and turns this as well.

The ecoplough (and variations of it) have been developed to allow shallow ploughing and to facilitate driving on unploughed soils. This method of ploughing does not compact the subsoil in the furrow. It also enables you to work with wide, low pressure tyres. Furthermore, shallow ploughing demands less pulling power and increases capacity.

Disadvantages are:

■ Tall green manures are more difficult to incorporate.
■ The ploughing of fields with deep post-harvest tramlines requires prior treatment.
■ Better steering skills are required.
■ On wet clay topsoils, on clay soils, slip can develop and pulling power is lost.

◀ Special mould boards with a screw-like action make a wider furrow possible. This allows the soil to be turned completely without increased horse power. In these kinds of furrows, a wide tyre can also travel at low pressure. This increases the pulling power and leads to less slip. The low pressure also reduces the load on the subsoil in the furrow.

Other main soil cultivations

Ploughing and digging are the main soil cultivation techniques. Mechanical ploughing is the older method, while digging is relatively recent. Subsoiling may be the preferred cultivation method on erosion-sensitive soils.

Digging

Digging machines are in use on sandy and clay soils. There are rotating and crankshaft digging machines. The advantage of this treatment is the increased capacity. In one pass the soil is made ready to sow and there are no extra headlands and final furrows to work.

Not every sandy soil lends itself to digging; sandy soils must have good structural stability and sufficient organic matter. You can quickly make light sandy soils too loose; they soon slump again and become starved of oxygen. Somewhat heavier clay soils are often dug with crankshaft machines. A lot of farmers combine digging with drilling winter wheat in one pass. Fine sandy loams are less suited to these autumn cultivations. The soil aggregates have a tendency to slake and the soil often slumps easily.

Combined machines can increase the capacity of soil cultivations. ▼

For digging in heavy soils, a crankshaft digging machine is usually used. This loosens the soil with digging spades, while rotating spades further loosen and mix the soil. ▼

Soil Signals

Subsoiling

Plant roots grow deeper than the cultivated layer. If the deeper soil layer is compacted, this can restrict root growth as well as water-holding and drainage capacity. With deep mechanical cultivations, it is possible to remediate deep compaction. However, the results of subsoiling are very variable in practice. Following subsoiling operations, natural slumping and the fracturing of worm tunnels and root canals can increase the risk of further compaction. Therefore, trafficking straight after subsoiling should be done only on low pressure tyres and only in good/dry conditions.

◄ A wide subsoiler point can break up a compacted layer. Use a subsoiler with a wide point. Routine subsoiling in the autumn is discouraged. Only subsoil if there is a clear reason, for example to loosen the tramlines. Under the tramlines a compacted layer could be present, which impedes the rooting depth. Subsoiling there can also improve drainage and avoid the build-up of standing water.

Subsoiling tips:

- On discovering a compacted layer, ascertain the right depth for subsoiling first.
- Do not carry out the work in a wet soil. Handle the soil at the working depth to see whether it will break or smear. A moisture content of 20 percent is good. Pliable and smearing soils are not good.
- Dig a hole and during the job, check that the subsoiler is travelling deeply enough and producing the required results under the compacted layer.
- Ensure that the layer is sufficiently broken up. The fissures that the subsoiler creates have to transport water and gases and allow access to roots.
- Establish a deep rooting crop after subsoiling, e.g. cereals or lucerne, to enhance the improved rooting ability.

Dutzi

Special subsoilers with wide wings lift the whole topsoil. Because soils on sloping ground can be at risk of erosion, this kind of equipment is well suited for carrying out cultivations in such locations; this is combined with a rotary harrow.

Because the top layer is not inverted, harvest remnants and the organic manures remain in place, and the risk of erosion in many cases can be reduced. This also reduces the erosion sensitivity of many soils.

Tyre pressure

Agricultural machines are becoming ever bigger, stronger and heavier. This increases the pressure on the soil. If the soil is dry, trafficability is high. In practice this is usually the case in summer. However, at the main trafficking times during sowing, applying manures and harvesting, the soils are not dry and are therefore vulnerable to damage.

It is not only rooting depth but also rooting density that is reduced following the use of high tyre pressure. ▶

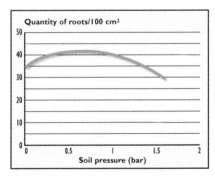

With a surface contact area of 2.5 m² and a pressure of 0.25 bar, you can apply slurry without compacting soils. ▼

Limit the damage

Damage caused by driving over vulnerable soil is mainly due to compaction. First and foremost, compaction means that pores are pressed closed in the soil. The amount of oxygen in the soil is thus reduced, resulting in restriction of root growth and even roots dying off together with a check in the growth of soil biota. This manifests itself in a reduction in water movement through soil, leading to poor nutrient and water uptake.

Avoid unnecessary traffic:

- Do not drive back across the field if the trailer is nearly full near a gateway.
- You may need to make more gateways to allow more points at which to exit the field.
- Fill the slurry tank or manure spreader with attention to the operating length and ensure that it is empty again when near a gateway.
- Adjust the size of the slurry tanker and the forage wagon to the average length of the field.
- Consider putting down a track on ground where soils are prone to structural degradation.

Rutting

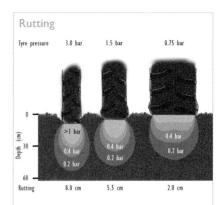

With a constant wheel load you can reduce the degree of rutting by tyre choice to change both soil pressure and the working depth of the soil pressure (wider and lower pressure). This will avoid compaction.

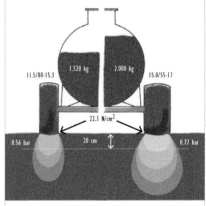

Both tyres give the same contact pressure. Although on the left the load is heavier, the pressure is divided over a larger area by the wider tyre. However, what is different is that the pressure reduction in the soil at the higher wheel load is less (with the same pressure). Relatively more compaction is found deeper in the soil.

Soil Signals

Working with low pressure

With low pressure in the tyres, you increase the contact area with the soil. This results in less rutting and less compaction under the same load. Keeping the tyre pressure low means a better soil structure and increased yields. Another benefit: it leaves you more days to work in the field.

Radial or crossply?

The ideal tyre for the road and also for the field is a combination of traction and speed. The faster the speed, the lower the required carrying capacity. Therefore, the demands of field use and road use are clearly different. A ridged tyre exerts more soil pressure than a supple tyre. Crossply tyres are more rigid than radial tyres. With a very rigid crossply tyre, ground pressure is 1.8 times more than the pressure in the tyre.

With the newest tyres you can drive on 1 bar tyre pressure on the road and in the field. Modified rims are required for these tyres.

Radial tyre

A radial tyre has 'bulging cheeks' with the correct (low) pressure. Alongside a reduction in compaction, this approach provides less wheel slip and saves 15 to 20 percent fuel.

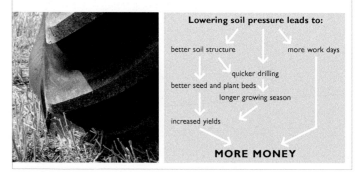

Lowering soil pressure leads to:

better soil structure → more work days → quicker drilling → better seed and plant beds → longer growing season → increased yields → **MORE MONEY**

Three-wheeler with a tank capacity of 14 m³ and a gross weight of 30 t. This is 11 t per tyre. With 110 cm tyres the pressure on the road must be at least 2.5 bar. With a pressure exchange system, the tyre pressure on the field must not be lower than 1.5 bar. Conclusion: despite a pressure exchange system, the pressure in the field from this machine is still too high. ▼

Low pressure and many tyres

More tyres increase the contact area and make low tyre pressure possible with the same machine weight. Multiple axles need to be steered to avoid scuffing in corners. ▼

Dual wheels are an advantageous way to reduce soil pressure. The tyre pressure has to be lower than with single tyres, otherwise you have not improved anything. ▼

Spring cultivations

Loosening soils increases spaces (pores) in the soil. This is essential for water and air supply and to provide space for the roots to grow through. With mechanical soil cultivations no more than a temporary structural improvement occurs, which is undone by precipitation, slumping, trafficking and grazing.

Genuine soil structure is formed as a result of the interactions of soil type, organic matter content and soil biota, which determine the shape, size and stability of aggregates. Good soil structure is also the basis for the formation of a good seed or plant bed, and you will have to adjust cultivations to match existing soil structure accordingly.

The length of the growing season is a factor in determining the yield. The earlier you sow the better. The opportunity for cultivating sand and reclaimed peat lands is usually earlier than on clay soils. Both soil moisture content and the amount of spring precipitation have an influence on the timing of soil cultivations. These cultivations are more easily achieved on sand and reclaimed peat lands. Levelling, ploughing, good drainage and a high proportion of macropores advance the dates on which cultivations are possible.

Preparing soil in one pass with low pressure (0.4 bar) is the best option. ▼

A rigid tine cultivator (ripper) can be more effective than the plough in some circumstances. However, on lighter sandy soils, these can slump and compact, so a plough is often preferred, as the soil is turned over in coarser lumps. Heavier sand soils with better structural stability lend themselves better to dense soil cultivations with a digging machine or a ripper. Main cultivations and seed bed preparations can be carried out in one pass.

Soil Signals

Clay soils

The greater the clay content of the soil the more difficult it is to break down natural aggregates. A heavy clay soil with low organic matter content is the most difficult to cultivate. Clay soils can only be cultivated effectively when the moisture content is right. If they are too wet they smear, too dry and they produce a cloddy tilth. When topsoil conditions become suitably dry for cultivation, subsoils may remain wet and susceptible to compaction.

Sandy soils

For sandy soils, spring cultivation consists of a main cultivation and a seed bed preparation operation. The main cultivation may be ploughing, digging or deep loosening with a rigid tine cultivator. Ploughing with a furrow press is an ideal method of making a sturdy seed bed. Seed bed preparations on sandy soils need to be carried out using towed rather than powered implements. Powered machines can destroy the existing structure and lead to compaction or slumping. Cultivations must take account of the organic matter content and the aggregate stability of the soil.

Cultivating and sowing in one pass

Combined implements, where cultivations and sowing /planting are carried out in one pass, can reduce soil compaction.
Requirements:

- Drive with a low tyre pressure (0.4 bar) or on fixed tramlines.
- Adjust the width of cultivations to the subsequent work pass of sowing or planting.

◄ *Sowing onions with 0.4 bar of tyre pressure on the whole seed bed. With dual wheels and the press roll between the wheels the tyre pressure can be reduced. In dry conditions you can even drive across the seed bed on 0.4 bar or lower. Evaluate the soil first: if in doubt drive between the seed rows.*

Autumn cultivations

In the autumn, after the harvest of early crops, there is an opportunity to level out fields that are uneven. The subsoil should be dry to prevent structural damage. The last cultivation should rectify any structural damage caused by levelling. Sowing of green manures is important if spring crops are to be sown, in order to enable crops to root through the loose soil. Also, maintaining a crop cover over the winter reduces the risk of water erosion on susceptible silty and fine sandy soils, especially on sloping ground.

Eradicating weeds

Germinated weed seeds which develop following the harvest are relatively easy to handle with a rigid or spring tine cultivator. Note that this treatment creates a new germinating seed bed for autumn-germinating weeds (grass, chickweed). The finer the soil is after cultivating, the more of these weeds will germinate. So cultivate the soil to create a fine seedbed in the autumn if you would like to eradicate weed grasses and chickweed.

Cultivating to give a fine seed bed on slump-sensitive soils with high rainfall can easily lead to compaction. Eradicating weeds can also be carried out with quick growing green manures such as mustard.

Rooted weeds can be tackled with a heavy duty spring tine cultivator with a wide goose foot. The cultivations have to be carried out along the length and width of the fields (two-way ploughing at right angles). Cultivating with a stubble plough is more effective, as all the roots are cut. In a dry autumn the cultivations can be repeated a few centimetres deeper each time. ▶

Can you

dig it?

Is subsoiling needed here?

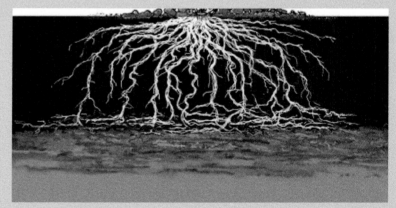

The roots are bending to the left and right at a depth of 25 cm because of a compacted layer at 25 to 35 cm. In order to improve rooting and water management, subsoiling with wide tips is recommended here at a depth of 35 cm.

Soil
Signals

Soil cultivations prior to cropping with green manures

Fields with early harvestable crops such as cereals, onions, tulips and peas are ideal for the subsequent sowing of green manures. How deep or how intensively the soil has to be cultivated depends on the soil type and the existing soil structure. The aim is to prepare the seedbed ready for the new crop: the green manure. Evaluate the topsoil first for structure and rooting. Adjust the soil cultivations accordingly.

Loosening soils and inverting
Straw or farmyard manure does not have to be incorporated deeply. So a disc harrow can usually work effectively. These machines invert the soil, incorporating the straw and manure shallowly. Simultaneously, a reasonably clean seed bed is created for the green manures.

Incorporating green manures

Incorporating green manures deeper than 5 to 12 cm is necessary if clay soils are ploughed for the winter. With a rye green manure in the spring on sandy soils there will often be a large quantity of green mass to incorporate, though not too deeply. If the green materials finish up in an anaerobic environment, they break down poorly and may release compounds that are toxic to roots.
Procedure:

- Do not plough too deep when incorporating green manures. Ploughing deeper than 20 cm reduces oxygen content in the soil considerably.
- Carry out pre-cultivations with a disc cultivator.
- A straw incorporator is used on the plough instead of a pre-furrow.

Ploughing and seeding in one pass
Implement combinations increase carrying capacity. By combining seed bed preparation and drilling in a single pass, the risk of compaction associated with a second pass is avoided.

With the disc harrow, stubble cultivations and drilling can be done in one pass. The disc harrow has a good inversion action that incorporates stubble remnants and organic manures. A green manure can be drilled at the same time. ▼

Drainage

Good drainage is the basis for good crop growth. In areas where water remains ponded on the surface or saturates the profile, it displaces air from the pore spaces. Under this oxygen-deficient environment much of the soil biota cannot breathe, and those that can work in anaerobic conditions can cause nitrogen losses through denitrification. In oxygen-deprived conditions the roots die back. A grass sward in a field with a high soil water table in the winter has its rooting depth restricted and can become drought prone in the summer when the water table falls.

Timely springtime cultivations also ensure a good start to the crop.

Wet soils warm up a lot more slowly in the spring compared to dry soils. In cold and wet soils, phosphorus therefore becomes more slowly available to the plant. Heavy clay soils become more difficult to cultivate as the soil moisture content increases and the risks of smearing and compaction are greater. Therefore, it is important to harvest root crops early in order to reduce the tare on the harvested product and any damage to the soil. On heavier soils and soils with a high water table, grading the surface towards drainage ditches is a good way of quickly transporting away a lot of surface water.

Excessive water...

In the spring good drainage is essential in order to lower the water table, improve soil bearing strength and avoid rutting. In the autumn this is important in order to harvest maize without structural damage to the soil.

A wet area can be self-perpetuating if it occupies a low-lying position and the soil texture is prone to instability. The soil lowers and slumps, which means that more water will collect there next time. With a lack of activity of soil biota and plant growth, the structure and the natural drainage will not recover. In a field, the area that remains wet the longest is often the limiting factor to allow access to the land. If you do not wait for the area to dry out, the soil will get more damaged by traffic.

Immediate subsoiling or cultivating with a rigid tine cultivator and the drilling of rye would have improved matters. Of course only if conditions were not too wet at the time of harvest! The cultivations and the green manures would have improved the drainage and avoided leaching of nutrients. Images like this will then be a thing of the past.

Soil Signals

Improving drainage

Under grassland, a soil is well drained if the average water level remains below 40 cm depth during the winter, and there is no persistent standing water on the surface. For arable and vegetable production, the ideal water level depth is 80 to 120 cm. Levelling the field and ploughing ensures uniform drainage and good soil properties. Optimal drainage is achieved by precise design of drain spacing and depth in association with ditches receiving drain outfalls.

▲ *A troublesome compacted layer where water collects must be removed to improve drainage.*

Improvement and maintenance of surface drainage with gullies or mole drainage improves trafficability and yield. ▼

Does the drainage work effectively?

Drainage and maintenance of drainage outlets ensure excellent drainage. Check that the outlets are working properly and that there is no sediment blocking them. A well functioning drainage system should transport 5 to 7 mm (5 to 7 litres/m2) daily. This can be checked by catching water as soon as the drains start running full bore.

This will measure the number of litres of water per second in relation to the catchment area of the drain.
For example, drainpipes 5 m apart drain a 100 m wide field. The number of litres to be drained with precipitation of 6 mm/day is 6 x 5 x 100 = 3000 litres. This amounts to 3000/(24 x 60) = about 2 litres per minute.

Deep ploughing, deep digging and deep subsoiling

Deep soil operations are mainly used to overcome problems at depth in the soil profile. The operation is often a one-off. These are deeper than annual seed bed operations, involving the use of a plough, digging machine or subsoiler. Applications are:

- Improving rooting depth on peaty and layered soils,
- Increasing carrying capacity on peaty soils,
- Lightening topsoil on heavy clay soils,
- Drainage improvements where troublesome layers are present in the subsoil.

Deep soil operations should only take place after a thorough examination of the soil characteristics and current condition of the soil layers. Two different operations are possible: an inverting action with the deep plough and a blending action with the mixing plough, mixing subsoiler or deep spader. Care is needed when operating at depth to avoid disturbing any drainage systems. The operation will destroy any natural pores deriving from old root channels or the action of soil biota.

Deep ploughing

Deep ploughing is possible to a depth of 2 meters. There are two ploughshares: the larger one brings subsoil to the surface while the smaller one returns topsoil down into the furrow dug by the former. The deep plough for ploughing subsoil up is mainly used to plough the subsoil to the surface. If a heavy topsoil is underlain by a lighter-textured subsoil, then this technique can be used to lighten the topsoil, although the disadvantage is that a more fertile topsoil can end up buried where it is of no use to crops. Ploughing humus-rich subsoil to the surface can impoverish the topsoil and make it more susceptible to erosion. Subsequent to deep ploughing, levelling of the ground surface is often required.

Deep ploughing with two furrows to a depth of 2 m. When ploughing at depths of more than one metre, the operation takes place in two stages: one ploughshare ploughs the topsoil down and another ploughshare ploughs the subsoil up.

Soil Signals

Mixploughing

Mixploughing is carried out using a plough with a single mouldboard. The shape and position of the mouldboard coupled with the speed determine the degree of mixing. When you change the position of the plough, a more intense mixing action can result. An advantage of this operation is that the topsoil remains partially in place on the surface.

Deep digging

Rotavators do not require as much horsepower as deep ploughing or deep subsoiling; these powered implements have a mixing action and a working depth of up to one metre. Rotavating is done on layered soils in order to mix troublesome sandy layers with clay layers. The operation is intensive and the soil makeup becomes more homogeneous than with deep ploughing. Deep digging with a digger places the topsoil apart whilst the subsoil is dug over, after which the topsoil is put back. A digger is also useful if the sand does not remain on the mouldboard during deep ploughing.

Deep subsoiling

Deep subsoiling is carried out when there are clearly troublesome layers in the profile which restrict water movement and rooting. Subsoiler legs with small points disturb only the target layer. The subsoiler legs with wide points have a mixing action. A wide point with a gutter-forming subsoil leg can mix the soil well, as the subsoil is pushed up along the leg to the top. The maximum working depth is 1.5 metres.

Deep digging with a rotavator to a depth of one metre. Mixing troublesome layers with other layers can improve the profile.

◄ *Deep dug ground. The mixing of clay and sand on a subsoil of sand is clearly visible. This is done in order to mix a shallow sandy layer with clay and thus increase water holding capacity and the depth of the rooting zone.*

Chapter 6

Maintaining soil fertility

Manuring is not only important as direct nutrition for the plant. The soil, soil biota and soil structure gain from an effective manuring strategy. Ultimately more nutrition is supplied to a well growing crop via the root system through the soil. A balanced pH is the starting point of good manuring.

▲ *Fine tuning in the use of organic manures and mineral fertilisers is required in order to guarantee crop yields in the short and long term and to adhere to laws governing fertiliser and manure use.*

Liming

The acidity of the soil is measured by the number of H^+ ions which are present in the free soil moisture (pH). An acid soil has a low pH and many H^+ ions in the soil moisture. Lime (both calcium- and magnesium-based) is able to react with the H^+ ions, whereby the soil becomes less acidic (pH rises). Limes contain carbonate ions which react with the H^+ ions under moist conditions in the soil, producing water and carbon dioxide. Chemically the reaction is as follows: $CO_3^{2-} + 2 H^+ -> H_2O + CO_2$.

The pH in the soil changes constantly. Causes of acidity are:

- Leaching.
- Crop uptake of basic nutrients.
- Conversion of ammonium into nitrate, whereby H^+ ions are released (nitrification).
- Soil biota respiration.
- Formation of acids from plant remnants (humic acids).
- Mineral fertilisers like ammonium sulphates and potassium sulphate.
- Use of slurry.

Soil
Signals

Most organic manures, e.g. farmyard manures, poultry manures and mushroom compost, act as liming agents as well as nutrient sources. There are examples of farms with a good soil structure and use of solid manures which rarely have to lime.

Liming agents

There is a range of diverse liming agents available on the market to counteract acidity in the soil. The effectiveness of these agents is indicated by a neutralising value (NV).

The speed at which a liming agent works depends on a few conditions:

- Fineness of the agent: the finer, the higher the reaction speed.
- Moisture content: the drier, the higher the reaction speed.
- Magnesium content: the more magnesium, the slower the reaction speed.

When spreading lime it is important to incorporate it immediately. Lumping of the material on application and hence reduced effectiveness of lime are thus avoided. It is also important to incorporate the lime well into the topsoil.

This fine, dry lime with low magnesium content is suitable for autumn and spring application. If there is a magnesium requirement, then an autumn application with a magnesium-containing limestone is the best option. ▼

Liming improves structure

Besides influencing the pH and the balance of cations on soil surfaces, an application of lime can also help to improve the soil structure. This works effectively on sands, sandy loams and heavy clay.

On slump-sensitive soils, the soil particles cluster poorly. As a result they easily fall apart and can form a kind of crust on top of the soil. Calcium ions in the solution and bound to soil clay particles (adsorption complex) limit this tendency to slump.

On heavy clay there is a strong bond between soil particles. The workability of the soil can then be a problem. With excessive calcium ions the bond between the soil particles is reduced, and this improves workability. Even with a decent pH, an extra application of calcium can have a positive influence on workability. Gypsum (calcium sulphate) does not affect the pH but does contribute to more calcium ions in the solution.

Building organic matter

Crop remnants, organic manures and compost are important sources of organic matter. Only organic matter that remains longer in the soil than one year contributes to building up the organic matter content. The remainder can be regarded as slow-release fertiliser. The fraction of imported organic matter that still remains after one year is known as the effective organic matter.

As a rule of thumb, in order to maintain the organic matter content at the 2 percent level on non-calcareous heavy soils, 1400 kg effective organic matter per hectare is required each year to a plough depth of 25 cm. It is assumed that the annual breakdown of organic matter in the soil is 2 percent. On lighter calcareous soils with a high pH value, with lots of intensive cultivations the annual breakdown is nearer 4 percent. This demand is equal to 2800 kg of effective organic matter per hectare per year. An increase in organic matter content is usually beneficial for the soils and the potential crop yield. However, care is needed as the trafficability and workability of the soil can deteriorate and the weed burden can increase.

A cereal crop like barley in the rotation is useful as a contributor of organic matter supply to the soil. ▶

Italian ryegrass used as a green manure after a cereal crop makes an impressive contribution to the organic matter supply with its roots. ▶

Can you dig it?

What can you see in this soil?

If you look closely, you will see the crop remnants of the barley and the roots of the green manure. These remnants make an excellent contribution to the organic matter supply in the soil and provide nutrition for the soil biota.

Soil Signals

Permanent grassland

Permanent grassland increases the organic matter content due to the absence of cultivations and through the organic matter supplied via organic manures and from the roots of the grass sward. For grassland on sandy soils, a one percent increase in organic matter gives about a €150 increase in yield per hectare, thanks to:

- a 25 kg higher soil nitrogen supply (SNS)
- 6 mm more available moisture
- ultimately 500 kg more dry matter yield.

Composting and organic matter balance sheet

You can work out whether the supply of organic matter is sufficient to compensate for the breakdown based on the supply and losses of organic matter on your own farm.

Step 1   Determine the total supply of effective organic matter in crop residues, green manures and organic manures throughout one rotation.

Step 2   Determine the losses of organic matter. As a rule of thumb, two to four percent of organic matter is broken down every year. This is roughly the equivalent of 1400 to 2800 kg of organic matter. The percentage broken down varies depending on the quantity and type of organic matter imported onto the field in the recent past.

Step 3   Calculate the difference between supply and losses of effective organic matter. If the balance turns out to be zero, the soil status is maintained. If the balance is negative, the soil draws on its reserves and organic matter content will decline.

Effective organic matter (EOM) of crop remnants, animal manures and green manures

Crop remnants	Supply of EOM (kg/ha)	Animal Manures	Supply of EOM (kg/t product)	Green manures	Supply of EOM (kg/ha)
Potatoes	875	Slurries:		Italian/Westerwolds ryegrass (undersown)	1,255
Sugar beet	1,275	Cattle	33	Italian/Westerwolds ryegrass (in stubble)	1,080
Winter wheat	2,630	Finishing pigs	20	Perennial ryegrass (undersown)	1,155
Winter wheat (excl. straw)	1,640	Sows	12	Red clover (undersown)	1,165
Spring barley	1,940	Chickens	31	White clover (undersown)	850
Spring barley (excl. straw)	1,310	Solid manure:		Oilseed radish, yellow mustard (in stubble)	850
Onions	300	Cattle	77	Vetches (in stubble)	645
Carrots	700	Poultry (litter)	143		
Short term ley 2 years	2,575	Broilers	183		
Rapeseed	975	Compost:			
Leaf vegetables	300–400	Mushroom compost	89		
Brassicas	1,150	Compost	183		
Root crops	400–600				

Source: NMI

Mineral fertiliser

Pay attention to the following items when selecting fertilisers:

- Crop requirement and nutrient supply via the fertiliser.
- Additional supply from the soil and available nutrients from previous cropping.
- The risk of losses from leaching or volatilisation.

In the right place

Phosphate fertilisers move particularly slowly in the soil. Band spreading of triple super phosphate can be used to target phosphorus more effectively.

Sulphur fertilisation

Sulphur deficiencies have recently begun to occur more often. This is a result of a lower amount of sulphur being precipitated from the air. If a soil has a poor sulphur supply capacity, then sulphur fertilisation may be necessary. Too much sulphur sometimes has a negative effect on the quality of the product and uptake of trace elements. Examples of sulphur-containing fertilisers are: ammonium sulphate, Entec, potassium sulphate, CAN (calcium ammonium nitrate) with sulphur, kieserite and Epsom salts.

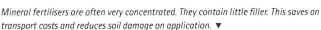

Mineral fertilisers can be simple (one nutrient only) or compounded (a number of nutrient-containing materials mixed together). This enables fertilisers to be selected to meet crop requirements, though it should be borne in mind that solubilities can vary. ▼

Mineral fertilisers are often very concentrated. They contain little filler. This saves on transport costs and reduces soil damage on application. ▼

Soil Signals

Spring fertilisers on grassland

Ammonium nitrogen in fertiliser is less likely to leach than nitrate nitrogen. A higher proportion of ammonium nitrogen in a fertiliser than the 50% in the most widely used, CAN (calcium ammonium nitrate), can lead to increased nitrogen utilisation or a higher yield at the first cut while using less fertiliser. Another ammonium-rich fertiliser is ammonium sulphate. The action of these fertilisers can be increased even more by the use of additives (e.g. Entec) which slow down the conversion of ammonium to nitrate. These fertilisers also include sulphur, so take care that this chemical is not supplied in excess.

Several fertilisers have an acidic or alkaline effect in the soil. Ammonium-containing fertilisers tend to acidify, while nitrate-containing fertilisers generally act to reduce acidity. The acidifying action can be counteracted by applying extra lime. ▼

Due to legislation, in some countries manure use is restricted. The consequently increased use of mineral fertilisers will increase costs. With proper soil management, nutrient efficiency can be improved and money can be saved. ▼

Slurry

Slurry is a liquid material originating in livestock housing and consequently has several possible application methods to land. Compared with farmyard manure it contains little organic matter but is a nitrogen-rich manure. The storage losses are minimal.

When spreading, especially on heavy soils, there may be a chance of damage to the soil structure due to the additional weight of the liquid contained in the tanker. As with any other field operation, the impact on soil is strongly dependent on the soil structure, the moisture content of the soil and the weather after spreading. Ask the following questions before spreading slurry:

- Does this fit in with the long term plan for this field?
- How much nitrogen does the soil itself supply (carry over)?
- Is mineral fertiliser, dry organic manure, farm yard manure or compost better?

Pay particular attention to the tyre pressure of the implement. This needs to be lower than 1 bar. Tyre pressure should always be determined in combination with the wheel load (tyre table). The degree of bulging of a radial tyre gives a good general indication. ▶

Influence on oxygen availability

The effects on the soil of slurry application can vary. As a check, open up a slit two weeks after application. Does it smell, or can you see blue areas? If so, anaerobic conditions exist, which can lead to nitrogen losses through denitrification. Ensure that the slurry is evenly distributed on spreading. Good mixing of the slurry before spreading results in an even application.

Nitrogen action on arable land

Around 50% of the nitrogen in cattle slurry is immediately plant-available (mineral nitrogen); in pig and poultry slurry 60% of the nitrogen is in mineral form. The rest is organically bound. About 95% of the mineral N is available in the first year with spring application on arable land by slurry injection, irrespective of the slurry type. The organic part is more slowly available; about 25% of the organically-bound N from cattle slurry becomes available in the first year, and about 30% from pig/poultry slurry. Often only the total nitrogen content of the slurry is known. With cattle slurry injected in arable land an estimated 50-60% of the total N is available, with 60-75% of total N for pig/poultry slurry. Autumn spreading is not recommended because of the large losses, amounting to a nitrogen efficiency of only 20%.

Two weeks after an application of slurry on a heavy clay soil with a very poor structure. After the slurry was surface applied, a dry spell occurred, causing cracks to develop where the slurry was deposited. This enabled exploitation by roots. A couple of weeks after spreading, check what is happening to the slurry.

Soil Signals

Nitrogen utilisation on grassland

The availability of nitrogen from slurry on spring application is similar to that on arable land: between 50 and 60 percent. This percentage depends on the proportion of mineral and organic nitrogen, the method of application, soil and weather conditions. With slurries from pigs or poultry the availability of nitrogen is 55 to 65 percent.

When to apply?

Start applying slurry to grassland when the soil warms up and is suitable for driving on. When spreading under wet conditions, compaction occurs and the slurry is applied to soil with a poor air supply. The soil may well be suitable for driving on as soon as early February, although it is still early in the year. Nonetheless, it is still better to wait a little longer before spreading, otherwise the slurry will lie too long on inactive soil and leaching of nitrogen may take place.

You often have to spread slurry at a time of the year when the soil is still wet and sensitive to compaction. ▼

By working with an umbilical system, soil compaction can be drastically reduced, as the tyre pressure exerted by the slurry tanker is eliminated. Because of the advantages of this method, farmers sometimes start using it too early in the spring. Check your tyre pressure! It should be 0.4 bar. ▼

Farmyard manure

During composting of farmyard manures up to 40 percent of the nitrogen can be lost relatively quickly. With a good soil structure you can use quite fresh manure, but with a poor soil structure this will soon lead to oxygen deprivation in the soil. Turning the manure a few times with a digger is a good composting method. When using a compost cover the manure can become too dry. ▼

Farmyard manure not only supplies nutrients but also contributes to the soil organic matter, feeds the soil biota and helps maintain soil structure. In the first year fewer nutrients are released to the plant than with slurry. On the other hand there is a slow release, especially of nitrogen and phosphorus, for many years after application.

Nutrient supply

Really effective manuring can only take place if the manure is sampled. That is why it is useful to have a complete analysis with the percentages of dry matter, organic matter, nitrogen, phosphorus and potassium. Then you know what you are applying. Nitrogen supply varies particularly strongly, potassium is quickly available, but phosphorus rather less so. The differences between loads can be large. Where the application rate is known, correct levels of top-up artificial fertiliser can also be applied.

Timing of spreading?

On clay soils under arable production farmyard manures are best spread in the months of June, July and August. Then when you sow a green manure the effects of the manure are optimal. On grassland spring is the best time to spread farmyard manure. If the weather conditions do not allow it, then do the spreading after the first cut.

What to watch out for when spreading

- Reduce coarse manure into smaller units by turning at least once.
- If possible, work with spreaders that reduce size.
- Limit soil structural damage by not travelling on wet soils.
- Fill the spreader with enough manure for it to be emptied in one pass there and back.
- Use low pressure tyres on the tractor and on the spreader.
- Avoid carrying too much and turn as little as possible.

Composition and nitrogen supply of solid manure

	N (kg/t)	P₂O₅ (kg/t)	K₂O (kg/t)	C:N ratio	kg N per t immediately available	kg N per t available in 12 months at 20°C
Cattle farmyard manure	6.4	4.1	8.8	14	1.2	4.1
Cattle slurry	4.4	1.6	6.2	5	2.2	4.3
Goat manure	8.5	5.2	10.6	13	2.6	3.8
Chicken manure	19.1	24.2	13.3	12	8.6	15.2
Horse manure	5.0	3.0	5.6	18	1.0	2.5
Pig manure	7.5	9.0	3.5	12	1.5	5.1
Mushroom compost	5.8	3.7	6.4	21	0.8	4.0

Types of farmyard manure

Horse manure loosens heavy soil, especially if it is humus-rich. It is less useful on a sandy soil since it causes it to become even looser. In addition, the availability of nutrients is limited because of the high proportion of bedding, straw and shavings.

Cattle manure is suitable for many soil types. On soils with poor structure, composting first is advised. Don't use fresh manure, especially if it is rich in straw. Store it for some months, and turn it up to 3 times - depending on structure/smell. When spreading, the manure should be 'short'. Don't apply large lumps.

Chicken manure is very rich in nutrients. The very high phosphorus levels should determine the application rate per hectare. Many arable farmers see chicken manure as a welcome addition to the organic matter levels and as a good supply of phosphorus, as well as potassium and other trace elements. Because it contains a relatively large proportion of nutrients per tonne its use can cause less structural damage than other more bulky manures.

Compost produced from cattle slurry can be broken up by hand into dry pieces. This makes spreading difficult. These solid manures are a useful aid in maintaining soil condition. But ensure that they are well chopped before spreading. ▼

The composition of goat manure *seems to be more variable. Sometimes this manure is very rich in nutrients, so you have to watch how much you apply.*

A straw-rich pig manure *with a good structure is an option on sandy soils. It is less useful on clay soils. The dung has a lubricating action on clay soil, which is not desirable on these soils.*

Compost

Compost has a beneficial influence on soil structure and the rootability of the soil. In the soil it breaks down slowly. Compost therefore contributes to maintaining and improving soil organic matter. In contrast to manures, composts are an immediate soil improver on a compacted soil structure.

Supply of nutrients

Just like animal manures, compost contains a significant amount of nitrogen. These quantities are released slowly. It is not the case that compost only delivers nutrients in the first year: it continues to release nutrients over subsequent years. With annual applications the capacity of the soil to deliver nutrients increases further. Compost also supplies other nutrients: the potassium in compost is 80 percent available in year one, and phosphorus 50 percent in the first year.

Green waste compost

Green waste compost and VFG (defined below) compost are the most important types. The ingredients used and the method of composting determine the properties of the compost. The composition of the raw materials therefore varies seasonally and from one region to another. Compost production is usually carried out at specialist facilities. Compost can be disease suppressant in action, but experiments with clear results are limited, so for the time being it is unreliable to use compost for this purpose.

Green waste compost is derived from park wastes, verge cuttings, ditch waste and waste plant material from agriculture. Green waste compost is prepared over a period of 6 weeks. The easily broken down material is easily converted in this period. Structural parts of plant material break down more slowly, especially if there is a high proportion of woody material.

Green waste compost preparation. Here the compost is usually arranged in huge windrows with active ventilation from the bottom. ▶

Composition and nitrogen supply from different types of compost

	N (kg/t)	P₂O₅ (kg/t)	K₂O (kg/t)	C:N ratio	kg N per t immediately available	kg N per t available in 12 mths at 20°C
VFG compost	8.5	3.7	6.4	12	0.8	4.8
Green waste compost	4.7	3.4	5.4	20	0.3	0.9
Composted bark	6.2	3.7	6.2	77	0.3	2.4
Potting soil	3.5	1.4	1.4	37	0	1.0

VFG compost

VFG compost is prepared from vegetable, fruit and garden waste. This compost is generally richer in nutrients and breaks down a lot more quickly than green waste compost. However, there is a lot of variation between batches; this is often associated with the season. Check the quality when purchasing. Chemical composition is not the only important factor; the compost should exclude other waste, including metals and plastics. In general, the quality of composts has vastly improved over recent years and the quantities of heavy metals have been reduced through general agreements within the waste sector.

Time of application

Compost can be applied throughout the year. Only VFG compost can give salt scorch, if you apply it in large quantities and close to the planting of a crop.

DIY compost?

Some farmers make their own compost. This requires expertise, work and investment. The compost is formed into windrows and is turned several times, often with a specialised composting machine. It can be covered with a compost cover.

▲ VFG compost delivery. VFG is important for supplying organic matter but also clearly delivers nutrients - more so than green waste compost.

In bulb production, VFG compost can play an important role in maintaining the organic matter content. ▼

◄ Green waste compost applied to a heavy, compacted sandy clay loam has put the worms back into action. It has also intensified rooting.

Chapter 7

Crop rotation

Crop rotation is required in arable and vegetable production and is also used in livestock production. In a crop rotation you plant the field with different crops in turn to limit soil-borne diseases. This helps to keep the soil healthy and the crops productive. The main question is: how do you manage your cropping plan and the crop rotation so that you can still grow crops on a healthy and fertile soil in twenty years' time?

▲ Cereals, especially wheat and rye, have a positive influence on crop rotations due to their dense and deep rooting.

Many crops suffer from soil-borne diseases. These are caused by nematodes, fungi and insects. Hence potatoes have trouble with soil fatigue because of nematodes, peas suffer from fusarium root diseases after garden beans, and sugar beet has problems with leather-jackets after grassland. In a rotation, crops are alternated, and the same crop only returns to the field after several years. This enables certain diseases and plagues to be controlled. In addition, crop rotation is useful in managing soil fertility, soil structure and in the suppression of weeds. Leguminous plants, for example, leave nitrogen behind in the soil. Deep rooting crops improve soil structure and crops that cover the ground quickly prevent weeds from developing.

Plant families

When designing crop rotations, the crops are considered in plant families. Mixing of families can keep diseases at bay that can arise within the same family.

- *Brassicas:* cauliflower, cabbage, broccoli, radish, forage rape, rape-seed etc.
- *Legumes:* peas, runner beans, green beans, clover, lucerne
- *Umbelliferae:* carrot, celery, parsley, parsnip, dill
- *Chenopodiaceae:* beetroot, spinach, chard, sugar beet
- *Asteraceae:* lettuce, endive, chicory
- *Onions:* onion, leek, garlic, shallot, chive
- *Solanaceae:* potato, tomato, paprika, aubergine
- *Cucurbitaceae:* cucumber, courgette, gherkin, pumpkin, melon
- *Gramineae:* grasses, cereals

Soil-borne diseases and plagues

There are a large number of diseases of which we know that the frequency of cropping can have a major influence on the degree of infection. These are nearly always caused by disease- or plague-causing organisms that are soil-borne and hence survive for some time.

- *Insects:* frit fly, bean fly, Colorado and beet beetles, aphids
- *Soil moulds:* root diseases, scab, clubfoot
- *Soil viruses:* rattle virus, tobacco rattle virus
- *Nematodes:* cyst nematodes and root knot nematodes
- *Bacteria:* brown rot bacteria in potatoes

With crop rotation you can limit the damage caused. Many harmful organisms are type-specific and remain at acceptable levels if the same crop is not grown annually. Some soil-borne diseases can rest for a long time in the soil, for example white rot in onions and rhizomania in sugar beet. Rhizoctonia in sugar beet is also carried in other crops like gladiolus and cereals. In a wide crop rotation, natural enemies also have a chance to develop.

◄ *Peas assimilate nitrogen and provide an opportunity to sow a green manure crop afterwards. Peas are sensitive to root diseases, so they should only be grown in the same field after a break of seven years or more.*

Two crop rotation plans

Cropping plan 1:3	Cropping plan 1:6
1. Consumption potatoes	1. Consumption potatoes
2. Sugar beet	2. Spring barley and green manure
3. Wheat + seed onions	3. Carrots
	4. Peas + green manure
	5. Onions
	6. Wheat + green manure
17% cereals	33% cereals
17% green manure	50% green manure
66% late harvest crops	33% late harvest crops

Evaluation

The 1:3 crop rotation does not contain enough crops that help to sustain soil condition. Potatoes and sugar beet leave low levels of crop residues and are harvested late. So the soil biota has no nutrition and the soil structure deteriorates. The risk of soil-borne diseases increases in this crop rotation. Deteriorating soil structure and inactivity of soil biota reduces rooting, which reduces utilisation of nutrients and moisture from the soil. Crops become more susceptible to diseases.

The 1:6 crop rotation shows a good crop variation. Crops such as potatoes, carrots and onions have been selected, which demand a lot from the soil. On the other hand there are crops such as cereals, peas and green manures that help to reinstate soil condition. Together with deep rooting crops which make resources from the subsoil accessible for the new crops, the long period of crop cover is also due to the large proportion of green manures.

◄ *Cropping of green manures contributes to an extended crop rotation. On intensive horticultural farms, the cropping of grass as a green crop is positive for soil health.*

Green manures

The cropping of green manure is indispensable where the rotation is designed to maximise nutrient recycling and to maintain a good soil condition. But green manures also do more; they contribute to the development of organic matter, feeding soil biota, stabilising soil structure and, in the case of legumes, fixing nitrogen.

Positive effects of green manures

Nutrient management
- Retention of nitrogen and potassium, which would otherwise have been leached.
- Nitrogen fixation in the case of legumes.
- Nitrogen supply into subsequent crops.

Soil structure
- Maintaining and further building up organic matter.
- Preventing slumping and erosion.

Water management
- Through evaporation of growing green manures, sandy soil is easier to cultivate in the spring.
- Improved drainage through more dense rooting of the subsoil.

Undersowing

Undersowing a green manure ensures better germination (soil contains more moisture), provides soil cover quickly after harvesting the main crop and saves a work pass in the autumn.

The following green manures should be considered for undersowing: perennial or Italian ryegrass, tall fescue, red clover, white clover, black medic and Persian clover.

Stubble sowing

With stubble sowing you sow the green manure immediately after harvesting the main crop. The advantage of this approach is that you can cultivate and manure the soil after harvest. Disadvantages are that the ground cover and the development of the green manures can be disappointing, especially after a late harvest. Sow green manures as early as possible: one day's growth in August is the equivalent of a week's growth in September.

Mustard grows quickly and is useful for suppressing weeds. A larger mass develops above ground than below ground. It can be sown up to mid-September. Mustard is a host to beet cyst nematode; use resistant varieties. ▼

Leguminous green manures like red clover, white clover, vetches and lucerne can fix nitrogen from the air, so less nitrogen needs to be applied.

In order from top to bottom: oilseed radish, English ryegrass and Italian ryegrass. When they are sown at the same time, the above-ground mass is identical, although below ground there are large differences. ▼

Soil Signals

Incorporation

A green manure needs to be incorporated properly in order to prevent re-growth. However, ploughing too deep (>25cm) is not recommended because this can cut off the oxygen supply to the crop, and instead of the breakdown desired, fermentation may occur comparable to ensiling. This can prevent it from being utilised by the following crop. To prevent fermentation and give a better distribution in the topsoil you can carry out cultivations with a stubble plough or disc harrow prior to ploughing. In the spring, crops on sandy soils need to be cultivated once or twice with a disc harrow, tined harrow or cultivator prior to ploughing.

After ploughing, a good distribution of green manure material throughout the topsoil is important. By using a furrow plough on the plough this can be done in one pass. The disadvantage is that the green manure finishes up in the bottom of the furrow. A stubble coulter on the plough does not incorporate the green manure as deeply and is therefore more beneficial for the breakdown of the green manure.

Sowing times of green manures

Sowing up to 15 August
- Perennial and Italian ryegrass
- Vetches
- Lucerne
- Red and white clover

Sowing up to 15 September
- Oats and vetches
- Perennial and Italian ryegrass
- Forage rape
- Mustard

Sowing after 15 September
- Rye or mixtures of rye and Italian ryegrass

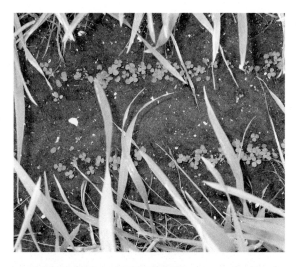

Can you dig it?

What do these crop residues tell you?

The crop residues have not been broken down but conserved. This 'ensiling' of green manures is often caused by ploughing in wet conditions.

◀ *There has to be sufficient light present at the base of the crop canopy for undersowing clover in wheat. Sow the clover under the main crop two to three weeks before the canopy of the main crop closes. The undersown crop then has a chance to germinate and form the first leaf before it becomes too shaded.*

Recipe for grass/clover

Possible variation: red or white clover
Red clover: only suitable for mowing. Unfertilised it produces the same yield as grass fertilised with 300 kg nitrogen per hectare.
White clover: for mowing and grazing. Unfertilised it always produces lower yields than grass fertilised with 300 kg nitrogen per hectare.

Recommended mix ratio for mowing only:
- 25-35 kg grass seed
- 5-6 kg red clover
- 3 kg white clover

For mixed mowing and grazing:
- 25-35 kg grass seed
- 4 kg white clover
- 2 kg red clover
  (optional: better crop establishment)

It is best sown on low-nitrogen stubble.
Apply 20 cubic metres slurry before sowing.
Aim for a pH of 5.5.

By forming an association with specialised bacteria, clover is able to fix free nitrogen from the air. Clover is therefore a pioneering plant for soils with a low nitrogen supply capacity. This makes clover useful on fields that are continually under maize cropping. These fields have low organic matter and low nitrogen supply.

In most systems it is beneficial to build organic matter in maize fields by growing grass clover mixtures. Dairy farms starting up on arable soils have to invest heavily in mineral fertilisers in order to maintain a good level of grass growth. As a result of the low disease pressure and low nitrogen supply capacity after arable cropping, grass/clover can increase dry matter production in these fields with low use of nitrogen fertiliser.

Crop rotation

Grass/clover is an ideal break within a vegetable or arable cropping rotation, and is also suitable for mixed farming with livestock, where forage maize is included. Subsequent cropping with forage maize fits in well with this type of rotation. Grass/clover crops produce well after a low-nitrogen crop of forage maize. In its turn, forage maize does well on the nitrogen that is built up in the soil by the grass/clover sward.

If you pinch the root nodules, as shown in this photo from the field bean, you can tell whether they are active by a pink colour. If they are white or green the nodules are not active. Nitrogen fertiliser application may be too high. ▼

Forage maize in a ripped grass/clover sward: without fertiliser but still a massive crop. ▼

Soil
Signals

Soil renovation

As well as supplying nitrogen, clover also helps to improve the soil's physical and biological condition. Beneath clover you will find up to twice as many worms as under grass; this increase in biological activity also helps to renovate soil structure. Livestock farmers on clay soils who have adapted to incorporate grass/clover into their cropping plan indicate that ploughing becomes easier. Water infiltration is higher (and run-off usually lower) under grass/clover than under grass.

Fertilising and yield of grass/clover

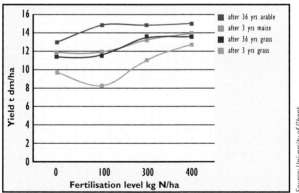

Source: University of Ghent

The effect of grass/clover is largest on arable land. Grass/clover that is sown after 36 years of arable cropping will be at higher production levels at low nitrogen application than with grass/clover that has been sown after 3 years of grass/clover, 3 years of forage maize or 36 years of permanent grassland. As a result of the low disease pressure and a low nitrogen supply capacity, grass/clover is very healthy when grown in intensively cropped soils.

◄ *The injection slots can still be clearly seen. With their thick roots clover is more sensitive to compaction than grass. The thicker roots find it more difficult to grow through the compacted pores.*

Clover can save 16 bags of CAN per hectare. ▼

Grassland renovation

Grassland renovation is usually carried out in response to the extent of the undesirable botanical composition of the grass sward. The decision can also depend on the need to level out fields or to improve drainage. An important criterion which is usually forgotten is the soil condition. Poor soil structure or rootability can be a reason for grassland renovation. On the other hand, a good soil structure can be a reason to delay the reseed or to choose another method of reseeding.

Downside of grassland renovation

However, grassland renovation does not only deliver improvements. There is also another side. Cultivation of a grass sward increases aeration of the soil, so the organic matter breaks down more quickly. The organic matter content and the nitrogen supply capacity of the soil are reduced. With the turning action of the plough, the layer that is rich in organic matter and nutrients is ploughed under and relatively poorer subsoil finishes up on top. It can take some time for the soil to recover.

Can you dig it?

What can you tell from this forage maize crop?

The stand in the middle part of this field is lighter in colour. As a result of soil levelling the richer topsoil in the middle of the field has been removed. So the maize in this area has fewer nutrients and less water available. In the adjoining grass field the levelling has led to local rapid growth of weeds after reseeding.

Areas of couch grass often indicate dried out sandy areas and poor grassland management (for example too heavy a cut or lumping) or poor rooting of perennial ryegrass. Establish beforehand what the cause of the deterioration in botanical composition is so you can avoid a recurrence in the future. ▼

Soil Signals

Think before you start

Evaluate a soil slice from below the grass sward, not only to assess botanical composition but also to evaluate its worm channels and soil structure. Is the soil structure good? Then choose a grassland reseeding method that avoids soil cultivations (spraying off and overseeding) or uses minimal soil cultivations (spraying off and reseeding following cultivation with a power harrow).

If the soil is compacted, it is important to use an appropriate field operation to loosen the soil. Do check what the reason was for the compaction to avoid a recurrence.

Productive grass sward

Grassland renovation provides the basis for a multi-annual, productive grass sward. The aim is to have a deep rooting grass crop in the soil with good drainage and a good supply of moisture. Therefore, the roots of the sward should grow into the soil as soon as possible. This is stimulated by also having nutrients below the topsoil. Fresh organic matter from green manures or farmyard manure provides the roots with nutrients and also stabilises the soil aggregates, improving rootability.

A deep rooting crop, like cereals, delivers organic matter deeper into the soil layers through its root system. Therefore, the following crop literally and figuratively will often follow the pathway of the previous roots. On organic dairy farms this is one of the reasons why a grain crop is sown before a grass/clover sward. Another is the optimal sowing time that this point in the rotation provides for the sward. In addition, combining the grass seed with 25 to 50 kg of spring barley seed per hectare provides a first 'frame' to the soil. Beware of compaction. In the early stages a reseed is very sensitive.

Where soil condition is good, overseeding of grass on a sprayed off grass sward is a good method of improving its botanical composition and maintaining the accumulated organic matter to a large extent. ▼

◄ *Alongside compaction by machinery and livestock, light sandy soils often have a natural tendency to slump. If the soil does not have the capacity to remediate the compaction itself, then soil cultivations provide the only solution.*

The rooting depth of maize without restriction can be about 120 cm. ▶

Maize cropping

With its tropical origins, maize loves soil that warms up quickly. Following germination and during the first growth spurt, the crop also requires sufficient moisture and nutrients. Maize is very sensitive to soil structure, so the starting conditions of the soil must be excellent with good drainage, no compaction and enough organic matter to maintain structure and water holding capacity.

Start with excellent soil

Forage maize has a negative impact on the organic matter balance of the field. It breaks down more organic matter than it leaves behind in stubble and residues. Given current restrictions on the use of organic manures it is not possible to replace organic matter sufficiently by manuring maize crops. Grain maize, however, leaves a lot of organic matter behind in crop residues.

In principle the organic matter content of a maize field will fall annually. This has consequences for the soil nitrogen supply (SNS). With a lower natural nitrogen supplying capacity, you will have to apply more nitrogen via manures.

Manuring on the basis of SNS has its limitations. When does the nitrogen become available? Mineralisation is difficult to predict.

Compared since 1966

In an experiment started on sandy soils in Belgium in 1966, continuous arable cropping is compared with permanent grassland and a rotation of grassland with maize. In the table it is clearly shown that the organic matter content and the nitrogen supply capacity of continued arable cropping declines strongly.

Soil analysis (0-10 cm) of four cropping systems

	Organic matter in %	SNS in kg N/ha
36 yrs grassland	5.7	159
3 yrs grassland after 3 yrs forage maize	3.3	93
3 yrs forage maize after 3 yrs grassland	3.8	102
36 yrs arable land	2.3	55

Can you dig it?

What is going wrong here?

Maize not only requires high quality soil for growth, but in wet harvesting conditions, soil structural damage can easily result.

Maize after grassland

An effective way to maintain good levels of organic matter in the soil is a crop rotation of forage maize followed by grass or grass/clover. This also reduces the need for added nitrogen in the maize phase. In the first year of forage maize after grass, up to 150 kg per hectare in fertiliser can be saved. In the second year this reduces but is still about 50 kg per hectare. The crop rotation of maize and grass/clover is rewarding, due to the nitrogen fixing clover thriving on the maize stubble.

Maize after green manures

By sowing green manures prior to maize you can achieve an increase in maize yield of 0.5 to 1 t dry matter with the same fertiliser levels compared to maize without a green manure.

Green manuring after maize

It is recommended and sometimes required by law to plant a catch crop after growing maize on sandy soils. This can be grass, forage rape or stubble turnips.

In practice the following four options give the best results:

1. Undersowing with Italian ryegrass when maize is knee height.
2. Sowing Italian ryegrass in the maize stubble.
3. Sowing forage rye in the maize stubble.
4. Sowing a mixture of forage rye and Italian ryegrass in the maize stubble.

More crop residues remain after cropping GEM (Ground Ear Maize) instead of forage maize; this can go a long way towards improving the organic matter supply. ▼

Manuring effect in maize

Forage maize in a crop rotation with grassland in the first year after cultivating requires only low levels of manuring. With continual cropping of forage maize there is clearly a manuring effect because of the lack of 'nitrogen buffer' in the soil.

Forage maize after 36 years forage maize cropping with manuring from left to right of 200 kg, 75 kg and 0 kg N per hectare.

Forage maize after ripping up 3 years of grassland with manuring from left to right of 200 kg, 75 kg and 0 kg N per hectare.

University of Ghent

In a mixture of barley and peas, barley helps to keep the pea crop standing. Grass can take up this function in a mixture of grass and peas. Both are usually harvested for forage or conservation. This mixture is used because of its protein content as a feed and the nitrogen supplying capacity for crops that follow the grass/peas in the rotation. ▶

Lucerne sown under a cover crop of oats. Lucerne is prone to weed problems and is often sown in mixtures with oats or Egyptian clover. Re-seeding of grass in spring can also be vulnerable to weeds. Sowing the grass seed alongside 25 to 50 kg of spring barley quickly provides a cover crop preventing weed growth. When the barley is cut, it will leave behind a valuable network of roots in the soil. This opens up the soil for rooting by the reseed and gives it a lead. To prevent re-growth of the cereals, avoid cutting the mixture too early. ▼

Cereal cropping mixtures

The mixing of different crops can occur for production and crop/feed quality reasons. An example of a crop mixture is wheat and field beans. This provides a protein-rich concentrate, but can also provide milling wheat with higher protein content than a monoculture. As well as the above ground advantages these cropping mixtures also deliver benefits to the soil structure, because the mixtures make better use of the rooting zone. As field beans (legumes) fix nitrogen from the air, both the wheat and the successive crop have enhanced nitrogen supply.

Other reasons why cropping mixtures with grain are used are weed suppression, minimisation of wind erosion and reduced risk of soil slumping. When sowing sugar beet, spring barley is sometimes sown as a companion crop at low density to counter wind erosion. When the danger of wind erosion has passed, the spring barley is sprayed off. Not all arable farmers know that the framework of roots in the ground of the young barley plants also has a positive effect below ground. Root system dynamics of this type are important in order to maintain the soil structure and stimulate active soil biota.

Wheat-field bean seems to be the most successful mixture with regard to both overall productivity and yield reliability. The crops also complement each other very well below ground: the nitrogen-fixing field bean increases the nitrogen supply to the wheat and the dense rooting of the wheat fills the gaps in the open rooting system of the field bean. ▶

Soil Signals

Maize in grass stubble

Although often experimental in nature there are several systems in which maize is planted in a living or dead grass sward. Potential reasons for the adoption of such bi-cropping systems include:

- Improving the carrying capacity of the soil in the spring when sowing and in the autumn during the harvest.
- Cost saving.
- Maintaining organic matter.
- Reduced nitrate leaching.
- Maintaining activity of soil biota.

▲ *A variation of planting maize in grass stubble is planting it in a permanent clover sward. Alongside weed suppression this delivers benefits linked to the fixation of nitrogen by the clover and increases organic matter and soil biota. This system has been tested for several years. It is clear that the root system of clover provides less competition to maize than grass. However, on drier soils the system is very sensitive to moisture competition which can be managed by cutting the clover very frequently.*

On his peaty soils Henk Pol plants forage maize with a rotavator into an established grass sward. In addition, slurry is injected directly into the rows of the maize. After germinating Pol cuts the grass with a specially developed mower several times until the crop establishes its cover. After the maize harvest the grass sward recovers by itself. ▼

◄ *On soils with low trafficability you can plant maize in the newly mown grass sward. The Hunter is designed for this sort of drilling operation. This machine pulls a slot through the soil by means of a rigid tine after which the seed is planted and the grass is pressed down. After germination of the maize plants the grass sward is sprayed off with Round-up.*

Crop protection products

Crop protection plays an important role in farm management. Since the 1990s the use of crop protection products has declined in most countries, though in general, large quantities per hectare are still used. Crop protection products can disturb the natural regulating functions of the soil-crop ecosystem. Detrimental effects (high environmental impacts) are often seen in pollution of groundwater and disturbance of aquatic life. Information about negative effects on the soil is limited.

Spray with air support to limit drift and for greater efficiency. ▼

Prevention

The production of a good crop protection programme is required by law in most countries and forms the basis of an effective approach to management of weeds, diseases and pest infestations. The plan should ideally include preventative measures. You can achieve this by working on the general conditions (strategic) and crop by crop plan (tactical) which minimises the presence of damaging organisms.

Strategic measures:

- Biosecurity: cover waste heaps, clean machines, remove diseased plant material.
- Crop rotation: with crops and green manures in space and time.
- Good soil structure and water management.
- Spray at the right pressures in order to minimise drift and to spray more efficiently.
- Support natural predators with ecological infrastructure (field margins).
- Select and time the type of soil cultivation (weed management).
- Do not use farmyard manure that contains weed seeds.

Tactical measures:

- Use healthy starting material.
- Choose tolerant or resistant varieties.
- Optimise nitrogen and water supply.
- Adjust row and plant distances.
- Combat root weeds on the spot.

Detrimental effects on soil biota

On apparently similar farms there often appears to be a great difference between environmental impacts resulting from crop and soil management. But overall, the environmental impact of potato and onion cropping is the greatest.

The quantity of crop protection products remaining in the soil depends on the speed of breakdown and the extent to which they bind to soil particles and the organic matter. Both the concentration of the product in the soil and the toxicity determine the risk to the soil biota. To get an insight into the damaging effects of specific crop protection products, CLM has developed the Environmental Yardstick (www.milieumeetlat.nl/en/home.html). This awards environmental impact points (EIP) to the effect that crop protection agents have on soil biota. The scale on the ruler is based on the toxicity of the product to earthworms. But hardly anything is known about the effects on micro-organisms in the soil. The risks to the environment are considered to be negligible if less than 100 environmental impact points are allocated.

Natural predators

In nature, diseases and pest infestations are often kept under control by natural predators. Farmers can make use of their services free of charge. However, the condition is that these helpers are not destroyed prematurely by spraying. You should take natural predators into account by paying extra attention to the choice of product and its selective use.

Crop protection products often with more than 150 environmental impact points

- *Challenge*
- *Amistar*
- *Pirimor*
- *Birlane granulate*
- *Linuron*
- *Gramoxone*
- *Reglone*
- *Laddok*
- *Lido*
- *Terbutylazine*

Tips for better practices

- Selective use of products. Protect natural predators by choosing a specific product.
- Limit drift and stay as far away as possible from field edges.
- Spray strips or parts of the field instead of whole fields. This allows natural predators to escape to an unsprayed area.

Sustainable
- *Less use of chemical products*
- *Adjust according to tolerances and within integrated crop management*
- *Natural products*

Unsustainable
- *Ample dose of chemical products*
- *Working sloppily*
- *Not following product instructions*

Beard growth of roots. This is the result of excessive root growth caused by eelworm infection. ▶

Nematodes and soil types

Most species of nematodes are found in the largest numbers in sandy and loamy sand soils. They are less of a problem in heavy clay soils. The worst crop damage therefore occurs on arable land with sandy soil and reclaimed peat land. But considerable financial losses can also be incurred on other soils, such as in planting stock cultivation.

Sandy loam and clay soil	Sand, loamy sand, reclaimed
Potato cyst nematode	Cyst nematode (potato, beet)
Beet cyst nematode	Root-knot nematode
Pin nematode	Trichodoride nematode (free-living)
	Stubby root nematode
	Pin nematode
	Xiphinema
	Longidorus

Controlling nematodes

Nematodes are generally thought of as harmful organisms. However, the majority of nematodes in the soil are useful, living on plant remains, bacteria, and insects. In the Netherlands there are 1200 types of nematodes; a hundred of these are harmful to plant growth, and about 25 are important for agriculture.

Damage

Nematodes feed at the root tips of several crops. With a severe infection the plant will stop growing or it will produce a lot more new roots, giving the typical furring or beard growth. In the spring when plants are in the germination stage the damage caused by nematodes can be severe and open areas may appear in the crop. Eelworm damage also affects crop quality (conservation) and some are mandatory quarantine organisms.

Disinfecting soil

Disinfecting soil can be done in several ways:

- Chemically. Use a coulter injector with dichloropropene or a banded injector with metam sodium. Granulate can be applied to rows or across the whole field to prevent seasonal crop damage with varying success.
- Water. Flooding a field for several weeks in summer reduces oxygen levels, killing most nematodes.
- Steam. Soil in glasshouses is steamed to kill the nematodes.
- Hot air. This is done by digging over the whole field intensively and blowing hot air at 800°C into the soil.
- Biologically. A heavy green manure is incorporated and made air-tight with film.

◀ *Open patch in the crop. Because nematodes have attacked the young plants, they have not developed.*

The chemical, water and steam disinfection methods kill off all soil biota. This may be beneficial for a short time because other carriers of disease apart from the nematodes will also be killed. Steaming also kills a large proportion of weed seeds. But if you kill off everything, there is a good chance that certain organisms will develop populations in an irregular way. The soil biota will be out of balance. In these circumstances there is a higher risk of parasitic fungi developing.

Serious infection

Do you have a serious nematode infection? Then get together with an expert to work out a strategy that fits in with your cropping plan, the soil type and the nematode.

Green manures

Green manures can encourage nematodes to multiply but they can also control them. Free-living nematodes in particular are maintained and even boosted by green manures. Some green manures can reduce numbers of cyst nematodes dramatically. These plants produce a substance that attracts the larvae out of the cysts. The larvae are then deprived of food and die.

Options:
- Sticky nightshade is a good destroyer of the potato cyst nematode.
- Forage rape is a good destroyer of beet cyst nematodes.
- Marigolds are a good destroyer of the stubby root nematode.

Prevention is better than cure

- Be aware of which types of nematode can occur on specific soil types.
- Examine root growth in poor areas of the field for brown root tips, beard growth and strong branching.
- Check for infection by taking soil samples.
- Implement a generous crop rotation scheme.
- Avoid infection by keeping contractors' or neighbours' machinery, infected plant material and infected soil off the farm.
- Provide plenty of organic matter.
- Encourage diverse and active soil biota.
- Ensure good drainage.

◄ Nematode destruction with water. The air supply to the ground is cut off and the nematodes suffocate.

Carrot affected by the stubby root nematode. You can clearly see that the tap roots have been affected, so the root is growing side roots and cannot develop fully. ►

Index

Soil Signals

MORE THAN 35 YEARS' EXPERIENCE IN SUSTAINABLE AGRICULTURE RESEARCH

the natural source of knowledge

The Louis Bolk Institute (based in Driebergen, the Netherlands) is an independent international knowledge institute promoting truly sustainable agriculture, nutrition and health. With practice-oriented research and advice we have contributed to the health of humans, animals, plants and soils and their interrelationships for more than 35 years. Our principal clients include the Dutch Ministry of Economic Affairs, the European Commission, the Netherlands Organisation for Health Research and Development, provincial governments, water boards, nature conservation organisations, foundations, knowledge centres and businesses. They value our comprehensive vision of sustainable agriculture, nutrition and health, and our ability to come up with system-level solutions. A selection of our main research themes: animal welfare, sustainable soils, plant breeding, agro-ecology, biodiversity, food quality and nature-assisted health. For a full overview of our projects, please visit **http://www.louisbolk.org/projects.**

'How much broader would be our view of life, if we could study it through reducing glasses?'

LOUIS BOLK (1866-1930) WAS A PROFESSOR OF HUMAN ANATOMY AT THE UNIVERSITY OF AMSTERDAM.

The Louis Bolk Institute stands for:

Pioneering research:
We do inventive, innovative and sometimes ground-breaking research.
Evidence-based results:
We use scientific methods and deliver tangible results.
Coherent methodology:
We follow a systems approach.
Applicable knowledge and solutions:
We offer practical solutions that can be directly implemented by our target groups.

On our website we offer a database of more than 1,850 publications (of which more than 600 are in English) by our institute staff members. Most of our publications are available in PDF and can be downloaded directly; see **http://www.louisbolk.org/publications.**

For more information please contact us by e-mail at info@louisbolk.nl or phone on +31(0)343 523 860.
www.louisbolk.org,
Twitter: @LouisBolkInstit

Roodbont Publishers

| AGRICULTURAL PUBLISHERS

Roodbont Agricultural Publishers considers its core business to be supporting agriculturalists by providing the right information at the right time. Its mission is above all to contribute to the long term sustainability of farmers and their working environment.

Publications from Roodbont can be ordered from bookstores or direct from Roodbont by phone: + 31 (0)575 54 56 88, e-mail: info@roodbont.com or from our website: **www.roodbont.com**. Many of our publications are available in several languages. You can order books in other languages from **www.roodbont.com**.

Crop Signals series

Weather & Crop Protection
ISBN 978-90-8740-002-6
84 pages

Soil Signals
ISBN 978-90-8740-157-3
96 pages

Potato Signals
ISBN 978-90-8740-130-6
112 pages

Other editions

Grassland Signals
ISBN 978-90-8740-046-0
96 pages

Pig Signals
ISBN 978-90-75280-77-7
96 pages

Cow Signals
ISBN 978-90-75280-65-4
96 pages

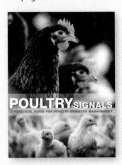

Poultry Signals
ISBN 978-90-8740-079-8
112 pages

For more information about these and other Roodbont publications please check our website: www.roodbont.com

Soil
Signals